SAI SPEED MATH ACADEMY

ABACUS MIND MATH

Excel at Mind Math with Soroban, a Japanese Abacus

LEVEL – 2

WORKBOOK 2 OF 2

PUBLISHED BY SAI SPEED MATH ACADEMY

USA

www.abacus-math.com

Published in the United States of America by SAI Speed Math Academy, 2014

The Library of Congress has cataloged this book under this catalog number:
Library of Congress Control Number: 2014907005

ISBN of this edition: 978-1-941589-05-2

Thanks to **Abiraaman Amarnath** for his valuable contribution towards the development of this book.

www.abacus-math.com
Edited by: WordPlay
www.wordplaynow.com
Front Cover Image: © [Yael Weiss] / Dollar Photo Club
Printed in the United States of America

Our Heartfelt Thanks to:

Our

Higher Self,

Family,

Teachers,

And Friends

for the support, guidance and confidence they gave us to...

...become one of the rare people who don't know how to quit. (–Robin Sharma)

Dear Parents and Teachers,

Thank you very much for buying this workbook. We are honored that you choose to use this workbook to help your child learn math and mind math using the Japanese abacus called the "Soroban". This is our effort to bring a much needed practice workbook to soroban enthusiasts around the world.

This book is the product of over six years of intense practice, research, and analysis of soroban. It has been perfected through learning, applying, and teaching the techniques to many students who have progressed and completed all six levels of our course successfully.

We are extremely grateful to all who have been involved in this extensive process and with the development of this book.

We know that with *effort, commitment* and *tenacity*, everyone can learn to work on soroban and succeed in mind math.

We wish all of you an enriching experience in learning to work on abacus and enjoying mind math excellence!

We are still learning and enjoying every minute of it!

GOAL AFTER COMPLETION OF LEVEL 2 – WORKBOOKS 1 AND 2

On successful completion of the two workbooks students would be able to:
1. Add any two to three digit numbers that involve carry-over or regrouping problems.

HELPFUL SKILLS

- Must have mastered LEVEL – 1 concepts
- Must have completed **LEVEL – 2 WORKBOOK 1 OF 2**.

INSTRUCTION BOOK FOR PARENTS/TEACHERS

Workbooks do not contain any instruction on what is taught within the lessons or how to use an abacus. All instructions are in the Instruction Book that is sold separately under the title:
Abacus Mind Math Level – 2 Instruction Book – ISBN 978-1-941589-03-8

HIGHER LEVEL

Thank you very much for using our LEVEL – 2 books. After you complete LEVEL – 2 by completing Workbook 1 of 2 and Workbook 2 of 2 please proceed to use our LEVEL – 3 books to continue your abacus training.

LEVEL – 3 books are **sold separately** under the title:

Abacus Mind Math Level – 3 Instruction Book – ISBN: 978-1-941589-06-9

Abacus Mind Math Level – 3 Workbook 1 of 2 – ISBN: 978-1-941589-07-6

Abacus Mind Math Level – 3 Workbook 2 of 2 – ISBN: 978-1-941589-08-3

WE WOULD LIKE TO HEAR FROM YOU!

Please visit our Facebook page at https://www.facebook.com/AbacusMindMath. Contact us through http://www.abacus-math.com/contactus.php or email us at info@abacus-math.com

We Will Award Your Child a Certificate Upon Course Completion:

Once your child completes the test given at the back of the workbook – 2, please upload pictures of your child with completed test and marks scored on our Facebook page at https://www.facebook.com/AbacusMindMath, and at our email address: info@abacus-math.com

Provide us your email and we will email you a personalized certificate for your child. Please include your child's name as you would like for it to appear on the certificate.

LEARNING INSTITUTIONS AND HOME SCHOOLS

If you are from any public, charter or private school, and want to provide the opportunity of learning mind math using soroban to your students, please contact us. This book is a good teaching/learning aid for small groups or for one on one class. Books for larger classrooms are set up as 'Class work books' and 'Homework books'. These books will make the teaching and learning process a smooth, successful and empowering experience for teachers and students. We can work with you to provide the best learning experience for your students.

If you are from a home school group, please contact us if you need any help.

Contents

SAI Speed Math Academy

HOW TO USE THIS WORKBOOK

Use this workbook after completing ABACUS MIND MATH LEVEL 2 - WORKBOOK 1 of 2. Work in the order given.

Each and every child is unique in his/her ability to learn. Sometimes a lesson might have to be repeated to get better understanding. You can erase the answers and redo the same lesson. On the other hand you may choose to move through the lessons quicker if child is an easy learner.

Each week's work is grouped together. Finish all the pages under each week before moving on to the next week's work. Work is divided for 5 days and you may choose to combine any number of days if you want to finish in shorter time. But, be very careful when you choose to do this, because children get overwhelmed easily when introduced to too many new concepts in a short time without having enough time to understand and practice. Use your best judgment since you know your child's temperament and learning capabilities.

After finishing a DAY's work check the answer and redo the problems with the wrong answer.

Wish you all the best!

FINGERING – Correct fingering is very important so, practice moving earth beads and heaven beads using the correct fingers.

WEEKS 11 to 16 – Big friend formulas for +5, +4, +3, +2, +1, and +10 are introduced. Students will work with 2 digit and 3 digit numbers.

WEEK 17 to 20 – Skill building

END OF LEVEL – 2 TEST – Wish you all the best!

KEEPING TRACK

TIME: Make note of the time it takes your student to finish each day's work.

GRADES: Correct their work and calculate grade. Let your student color the stars next to each day's work. This will keep them engaged and encouraged.

GOAL: As student progresses through the week they should be able to do their work in less time with more accuracy.

HOW TO CALCULATE GRADE?

$$\frac{\text{Number of correct problems}}{\text{Total number of problems}} \times 100 = \text{Percentage scored}$$

GRADES

GRADE	PERCENTAGE	STAR COLOR
A+	96-100 EXTRAORDINARY	GOLD
A	91-95 EXCELLENT	
B+	86-90 AWESOME	SILVER
B	81-85 GOOD	
C	76-80 CONGRATULATIONS	BROWN
C+	70-75 CONGRATULATIONS	

FINGERING

JOB OF THE THUMB (1):

A. Used to push the Earth Beads up to the beam, adding them to the game (ADD).

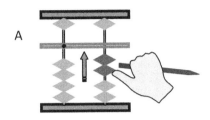

JOB OF THE POINTER FINGER (3):

1. Used to push the Earth Beads away from the beam, removing them from the game (MINUS).
2. Used to push the Heaven bead down to touch the beam, adding it to the game (ADD).
3. Used to push the Heaven bead away from the beam, removing it from the game (MINUS).

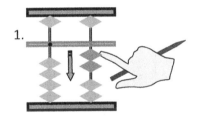 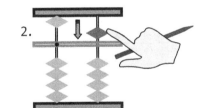 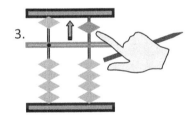

JOB OF THE OTHER THREE FINGERS:

Use your other three fingers to hold your pencil with the point facing down or away from you.

WEEK 11 – LESSON 10 – INTRODUCING + 5 CONCEPT

LESSON 10 – PRACTICE WORK

+ 5 = + 10 – 5

Use Abacus

DAY 1 – MONDAY

TIME: _____min _____sec   Accuracy _____/32 ☆

1	2	3	4	5	6	7	8	
35	44	11	52	29	55	23	29	11:1
05	35	15	09	26	25	15	15	
22	05	05	35	50	50	17	14	

1	2	3	4	5	6	7	8	
74	49	64	77	27	14	48	79	11:2
56	75	55	15	25	33	15	75	
18	08	55	55	08	05	59	55	

1	2	3	4	5	6	7	8	
33	39	41	36	12	12	15	47	11:3
35	15	55	55	16	55	61	05	
08	09	55	- 70	35	15	15	16	
- 55	50	55	47	52	- 82	54	55	

1	2	3	4	5	6	7	8	
15	54	18	35	15	37	288	345	11:4
17	13	15	15	16	16	155	123	
15	05	38	95	29	15	92	55	
05	55	59	05	54	85	55	- 313	

www.abacus-math.com

DAY 2 – TUESDAY

TIME: _____ min _____ sec   Accuracy _____ /16   ☆

1	2	3	4	5	6	7	8
35	25	35	23	28	29	37	42
- 15	25	25	25	15	15	15	25
19	15	37	08	27	35	19	05
- 05	15	55	06	- 60	06	- 30	05

11:5

1	2	3	4	5	6	7	8
55	27	27	31	11	17	304	169
- 34	- 15	25	57	45	18	274	175
45	09	15	50	17	14	70	11
85	- 21	- 44	57	53	15	05	- 223

11:6

DAY 3 – WEDNESDAY

TIME: _____ min _____ sec   Accuracy _____ /16   ☆

1	2	3	4	5	6	7	8
55	19	33	19	55	19	57	29
57	45	46	16	- 14	46	15	25
56	07	- 39	25	25	15	05	56
- 65	- 71	16	- 30	55	58	75	95

11:7

1	2	3	4	5	6	7	8
66	11	33	16	65	158	315	293
85	25	15	37	55	95	75	164
24	07	09	16	55	02	- 240	55
75	18	55	55	85	98	59	- 312

11:8

DAY 4 – THURSDAY

TIME: _____ min _____ sec   Accuracy _____ /16

1	2	3	4	5	6	7	8
75	45	23	17	59	16	29	18
15	45	22	05	25	15	45	45
05	- 60	15	45	07	17	05	12
55	38	59	- 16	50	18	- 24	75

11:9

1	2	3	4	5	7	6	8
14	44	14	64	76	45	355	351
16	22	57	59	55	75	54	155
15	05	05	65	55	57	45	- 306
15	25	09	55	07	76	55	55
19	- 84	- 21	- 43	- 91	80	- 404	95

11:10

DAY 5 – FRIDAY

TIME: _____ min _____ sec   Accuracy _____ /16

1	2	3	4	5	6	7	8
45	25	44	39	94	45	25	21
15	15	55	87	55	25	17	46
15	35	- 98	55	15	79	25	15
65	- 41	35	- 30	56	15	85	75
- 40	06	35	50	08	51	- 12	97

11:11

1	2	3	4	5	6	7	8
37	27	55	290	909	141	435	178
25	19	56	57	- 605	55	105	56
23	25	75	65	65	59	95	165
57	03	- 51	155	155	70	175	- 232
- 42	- 33	15	- 123	- 204	28	- 810	58

11:12

www.abacus-math.com

LESSON 10 – MIND MATH PRACTICE WORK

 Visualize

DAY 1 – MONDAY

Accuracy _____/10

1	2	3	4	5	6	7	8	9	10	
03	04	35	32	11	52	45	25	59	54	11:13
01	15	05	55	55	50	15	25	15	05	
05	05	25	05	05	05	50	50	25	50	

DAY 2 – TUESDAY

Accuracy _____/10

1	2	3	4	5	6	7	8	9	10	
57	25	44	99	55	19	08	15	48	29	11:14
50	52	15	50	11	15	06	35	05	55	
05	05	50	05	80	17	05	70	50	51	

DAY 3 – WEDNESDAY

Accuracy _____/10

1	2	3	4	5	6	7	8	9	10	
				12	21	17	54	19	50	11:15
55	66	77	66	63	05	05	25	56	50	
14	15	- 25	50	70	35	55	- 64	09	80	
05	50	50	35	05	50	- 64	55	50	- 160	

DAY 4 – THURSDAY

Accuracy _____/10

1	2	3	4	5	6	7	8	9	10	
				84	95	54	65	55	24	11:16
89	95	88	51	05	50	56	05	08	25	
05	- 44	77	54	05	20	57	08	56	25	
50	50	05	15	- 63	05	- 26	- 75	- 09	- 63	

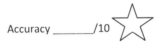

Accuracy _____/20 ☆

1	2	3	4	5	6	7	8	9	10
41	36	23	47	54	86	99	49	89	49
15	70	74	17	54	05	- 52	85	- 15	78
41	56	51	50	05	50	05	11	- 52	15
- 55	- 51	15	- 14	38	10	- 22	05	41	09

11:17 © SAI Speed Math Academy, USA

1	2	3	4	5	6	7	8	9	10
18	94	85	77	99	76	83	55	97	56
25	53	95	50	50	50	55	80	- 56	53
54	- 11	07	25	15	05	15	15	45	45
- 23	- 15	- 56	- 32	- 54	24	- 13	70	55	- 51

11:18 © SAI Speed Math Academy, USA

LESSON 10 – DICTATION

DICTATION: Dictation is when teacher or parent calls out a series of numbers and the child listens to the numbers and does the calculation in mind or on the abacus.

DO 6 PROBLEMS A DAY and write answers below.
Students: Try to calculate the dictated problems in mind.
Teachers: Dictate problems from abacus math part of this week's homework.

1	2	3	4	5	6	7	8	9	10

11	12	13	14	15	16	17	18	19	20

21	22	23	24	25	26	27	28	29	30

SUDOKU

3	5			1	2
1		2	6		3
	1			3	
	2			4	
2		5	1		4
4	6			2	5

Fill in with numbers from 1 to 6. Make sure numbers do not repeat within each column, row or block.

WORD SEARCH

PENCIL
STORY
PAPER
FRIEND
ERASER
BOOKS
TEACHER
SPORTS
DANCER
LAB
PEER
GARDEN
PAD
WRITE

```
R  E  P  A  P  E  T  I  R  W
P  O  O  K  S  K  O  O  B  P
A  G  R  K  R  S  N  A  A  E
D  A  E  F  R  I  E  N  D  N
A  R  H  D  N  I  V  O  G  C
M  D  C  E  R  A  S  E  R  I
U  E  A  S  P  O  R  T  S  L
R  N  E  R  E  S  N  A  K  B
A  A  T  D  A  N  C  E  R  A
S  T  O  R  Y  R  E  E  P  L
```

Write a story about your school and try to use as many words as possible from the above word list.

WEEK 12 – LESSON 11 – INTRODUCING +4 CONCEPT

LESSON 11 – PRACTICE WORK

+ 4 = + 10 – 6

Use Abacus

DAY 1 – MONDAY

TIME: _____ min _____ sec   Accuracy _____ /32

1	2	3	4	5	6	7	8
34	55	38	49	17	88	75	57
04	92	24	09	24	45	44	14
04	14	50	14	69	24	44	44

12:1

1	2	3	4	5	6	7	8
86	49	64	77	18	95	19	49
46	04	44	47	44	48	34	16
18	58	47	26	43	11	90	- 44

12:2

1	2	3	4	5	6	7	8
07	17	19	35	21	27	63	17
- 04	24	04	14	36	- 14	77	35
25	08	63	14	14	36	11	29
24	14	44	70	44	34	84	60

12:3

1	2	3	4	5	6	7	8
24	16	45	55	33	53	536	344
33	14	09	98	24	17	- 404	342
97	09	13	34	97	45	96	- 405
- 21	14	66	44	- 14	38	44	44

12:4

© SAI Speed Math Academy, USA

Pg 10

DAY 2 – TUESDAY

TIME: _____ min _____ sec   Accuracy _____/16 ☆

1	2	3	4	5	6	7	8	
36	15	11	19	15	99	58	16	
44	14	24	14	17	54	24	34	
05	14	- 15	29	14	14	46	59	12:5
94	- 13	14	45	48	07	25	45	
04	19	14	- 04	44	- 32	- 13	- 20	

1	2	3	4	5	6	7	8	
56	18	65	49	96	47	959	457	
04	44	- 24	10	64	- 14	- 600	- 314	
15	- 20	37	- 24	06	- 12	154	44	12:6
05	13	- 11	- 14	47	- 11	32	64	
45	96	87	- 21	- 13	90	07	- 231	

DAY 3 – WEDNESDAY

TIME: _____ min _____ sec   Accuracy _____/16 ☆

1	2	3	4	5	6	7	8	
16	17	25	36	36	59	28	36	
17	05	29	58	44	- 14	34	24	
09	36	14	44	59	23	45	29	12:7
04	04	47	15	06	44	47	74	
04	45	- 11	- 33	- 43	- 12	- 14	- 62	

1	2	3	4	5	6	7	8	
68	86	45	44	28	209	359	179	
75	54	24	14	16	044	264	247	
24	17	14	26	16	- 101	- 300	364	12:8
14	- 23	42	42	05	243	62	148	
- 40	17	- 21	- 13	45	45	49	- 904	

DAY 4 – THURSDAY

TIME: _____ min _____ sec   Accuracy _____ /16 ☆

1	2	3	4	5	6	7	8
69	39	24	27	38	66	25	19
44	14	74	26	14	- 20	- 14	46
16	18	46	54	09	18	55	- 34
28	24	11	44	- 41	07	48	15
- 33	- 32	- 43	- 11	55	47	- 11	04

12:9

1	2	3	4	5	7	6	8
63	39	63	32	26	592	515	148
24	24	26	19	47	- 440	- 304	125
48	07	04	18	25	97	155	44
46	08	- 30	14	54	04	84	44
- 30	18	79	57	73	97	- 210	49

12:10

DAY 5 – FRIDAY

TIME: _____ min _____ sec   Accuracy _____ /16 ☆

1	2	3	4	5	6	7	8
65	27	35	14	65	39	34	155
25	14	- 12	94	89	24	10	96
84	15	14	14	18	25	- 24	25
- 40	15	14	15	44	- 40	12	47
- 34	28	- 21	16	34	14	- 32	33

12:11

1	2	3	4	5	6	7	8
17	49	33	47	65	63	526	555
19	04	47	07	05	44	- 401	- 214
28	07	06	31	06	55	49	15
14	85	08	49	13	04	52	98
54	07	- 74	- 32	06	84	24	- 333

12:12

www.abacus-math.com

LESSON 11 – MIND MATH PRACTICE WORK

DAY 1 – MONDAY

Accuracy _____/10 ☆

1	2	3	4	5	6	7	8	9	10	
14	24	33	44	11	22	39	35	09	65	12:13
04	44	35	34	04	53	04	26	64	49	
44	04	24	05	44	40	12	40	42	- 13	

DAY 2 – TUESDAY

Accuracy _____/10 ☆

1	2	3	4	5	6	7	8	9	10	
38	14	67	06	08	09	29	19	49	56	12:14
19	34	44	18	45	44	45	47	46	81	
14	44	45	41	09	45	04	18	40	04	
40	04	07	50	- 32	- 85	04	41	- 04	11	

DAY 3 – WEDNESDAY

Accuracy _____/10 ☆

1	2	3	4	5	6	7	8	9	10	
55	16	77	66	92	75	15	29	73	24	12:15
- 22	66	- 13	50	04	06	39	34	40	43	
55	04	41	34	30	- 30	34	82	04	55	
44	40	45	- 10	18	90	45	- 41	58	44	

DAY 4 – THURSDAY

Accuracy _____/10 ☆

1	2	3	4	5	6	7	8	9	10	
85	95	88	25	48	61	15	59	75	99	12:16
05	- 44	- 34	16	04	49	16	- 32	- 31	54	
40	25	11	11	05	49	24	04	14	- 21	
- 30	44	47	90	- 17	- 36	58	32	54	08	

Accuracy _____/20 ☆

1	2	3	4	5	6	7	8	9	10
55	19	49	22	55	46	59	61	35	32
- 54	24	74	44	92	64	04	27	49	49
49	49	01	60	04	55	07	60	41	42
- 20	- 50	11	24	- 11	- 24	- 70	07	- 22	15

12:17 © SAI Speed Math Academy, USA

1	2	3	4	5	6	7	8	9	10
91	52	54	59	45	34	99	27	54	39
44	09	83	60	76	53	- 14	24	- 41	15
07	06	05	34	44	04	- 71	95	78	23
- 42	14	- 41	- 13	80	- 40	36	08	- 80	74

12:18 © SAI Speed Math Academy, USA

LESSON 11 – DICTATION

DICTATION: Dictation is when teacher or parent calls out a series of numbers and the child listens to the numbers and does the calculation in mind or on the abacus.

DO 6 PROBLEMS A DAY and write answers below.

Students: Try to calculate the dictated problems in mind.

Teachers: Dictate problems from abacus math part of this week's homework.

1	2	3	4	5	6	7	8	9	10

11	12	13	14	15	16	17	18	19	20

21	22	23	24	25	26	27	28	29	30

SUDOKU

5	2			6	4
		1	5		
1	4			2	6
		2	4		
3	5			4	1
2		4	6		3

Fill in with numbers from 1 to 6. Make sure numbers do not repeat within each column, row or block.

MIRROR IMAGE

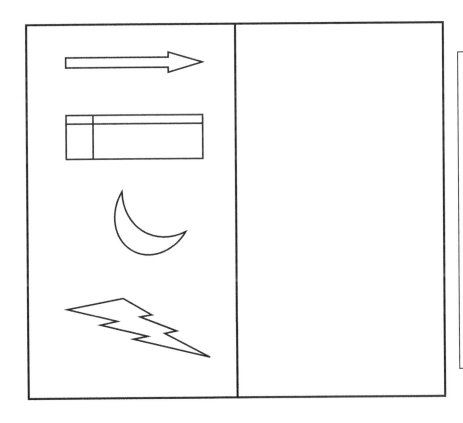

Draw the mirror images of the shapes on the other side of the line and color them. Use a mirror to see how the mirror image of each shape looks like.

Example:

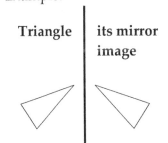

Triangle | its mirror image

WEEK 13 – LESSON 12 – INTRODUCING +3 CONCEPT

LESSON 12 – PRACTICE WORK

+ 3 = + 10 – 7

Use Abacus

DAY 1 – MONDAY

TIME: _____min _____sec   Accuracy _____/32 ☆

1	2	3	4	5	6	7	8
38	29	35	38	49	94	79	99
- 14	13	33	03	03	33	- 41	36
03	30	13	15	- 31	23	13	15

13:1

1	2	3	4	5	6	7	8
66	44	64	25	39	59	78	83
24	55	13	47	13	73	- 34	34
30	33	35	33	92	- 32	11	37

13:2

1	2	3	4	5	6	7	8
48	58	58	31	38	33	25	34
13	14	33	34	24	24	51	14
24	50	34	19	24	37	03	43
33	23	- 13	30	33	35	34	- 61

13:3

1	2	3	4	5	6	7	8
75	16	58	56	57	29	79	188
33	34	- 14	56	41	23	33	33
43	49	23	26	51	- 11	63	- 210
54	33	43	13	13	69	53	33

13:4

DAY 2 – TUESDAY

TIME: _____ min _____ sec   Accuracy _____ /16 ☆

1	2	3	4	5	6	7	8	
38	78	19	17	16	29	29	89	
43	35	43	13	08	33	45	38	
04	- 11	03	08	09	35	03	23	13:5
03	07	33	13	- 22	35	03	19	
- 75	46	53	25	39	- 32	- 40	83	

1	2	3	4	5	6	7	8	
49	88	28	28	78	95	381	395	
46	43	36	43	36	34	33	233	
33	- 20	83	- 20	14	34	36	23	13:6
- 11	63	35	28	35	09	09	- 411	
33	33	33	73	- 23	- 61	93	30	

DAY 3 – WEDNESDAY

TIME: _____ min _____ sec   Accuracy _____ /16 ☆

1	2	3	4	5	6	7	8	
34	39	45	99	85	36	49	94	
33	43	23	- 24	38	18	14	33	
- 20	08	13	37	65	15	13	26	13:7
16	- 70	- 10	55	63	50	- 70	14	
27	26	38	47	- 11	33	46	- 23	

1	2	3	4	5	6	7	8	
17	62	29	66	87	97	296	499	
33	- 20	13	03	47	64	234	34	
17	35	16	83	45	17	46	54	13:8
03	38	27	- 11	33	43	- 21	67	
39	35	- 61	24	- 11	34	55	89	

DAY 4 – THURSDAY

TIME: _____ min _____ sec   Accuracy _____ /16

1	2	3	4	5	6	7	8
96	55	37	49	61	76	64	398
37	99	57	13	57	52	81	136
44	21	35	78	74	54	45	02
- 33	38	24	75	36	35	36	18
18	92	- 13	38	- 17	37	- 14	96

13:9

1	2	3	4	5	7	6	8
46	19	43	15	33	53	298	277
23	13	09	47	24	17	130	133
83	33	16	37	07	08	39	44
08	06	04	63	23	34	31	79
03	- 31	- 22	88	33	12	35	08

13:10

DAY 5 – FRIDAY

TIME: _____ min _____ sec   Accuracy _____ /16

1	2	3	4	5	6	7	8
19	77	67	78	46	25	74	191
43	34	66	34	73	18	46	330
73	71	66	52	39	11	23	55
43	45	55	- 21	15	93	33	- 201
56	37	33	17	33	13	- 42	159

13:11

1	2	3	4	5	6	7	8
25	28	09	66	18	19	56	288
35	33	03	06	33	33	58	43
46	27	08	53	38	94	41	65
37	38	05	08	35	05	98	34
- 42	46	09	17	- 22	- 30	73	37

13:12

LESSON 12 – MIND MATH PRACTICE WORK

Visualize

DAY 1 – MONDAY

Accuracy _____ /10 ⭐

1	2	3	4	5	6	7	8	9	10
13	23	33	33	81	33	67	34	09	44
03	33	35	34	04	35	03	06	63	53
33	03	03	03	30	23	30	33	42	33

13:13 © SAI Speed Math Academy, USA

DAY 2 – TUESDAY

Accuracy _____ /10 ⭐

1	2	3	4	5	6	7	8	9	10
58	15	66	07	38	29	29	19	49	69
39	33	33	31	35	33	35	37	36	73
30	43	33	31	03	35	56	58	35	13
03	03	05	- 44	- 32	- 83	03	36	33	95

13:14 © SAI Speed Math Academy, USA

DAY 3 – WEDNESDAY

Accuracy _____ /10 ⭐

1	2	3	4	5	6	7	8	9	10
37	74	19	28	83	61	14	59	55	69
07	03	03	03	30	93	34	- 31	- 21	84
14	30	55	27	03	31	03	03	55	- 20
53	44	43	80	55	- 12	99	32	63	17

13:15 © SAI Speed Math Academy, USA

DAY 4 – THURSDAY

Accuracy _____ /10 ⭐

1	2	3	4	5	6	7	8	9	10
99	19	49	44	35	39	59	67	39	32
- 54	33	03	33	93	13	03	23	23	33
33	09	08	33	13	19	13	- 40	73	52
- 20	- 50	73	90	57	40	17	80	- 22	33

13:16 © SAI Speed Math Academy, USA

DAY 5 – FRIDAY

Accuracy _____/20 ⭐

1	2	3	4	5	6	7	8	9	10
35	54	98	57	90	17	22	47	98	34
50	15	- 33	23	39	35	26	40	- 24	15
50	56	75	30	18	32	03	30	73	03
17	30	- 40	52	64	32	- 11	33	13	- 22

13:17 © SAI Speed Math Academy, USA

1	2	3	4	5	6	7	8	9	10
34	31	28	85	51	60	55	99	84	78
32	37	35	- 11	12	15	90	50	32	50
32	60	13	40	85	30	07	13	22	14
53	26	48	16	13	48	63	- 32	13	- 40

13:18 © SAI Speed Math Academy, USA

LESSON 12 – DICTATION

DICTATION: Dictation is when teacher or parent calls out a series of numbers and the child listens to the numbers and does the calculation in mind or on the abacus.

DO 6 PROBLEMS A DAY and write answers below.
Students: Try to calculate the dictated problems in mind.
Teachers: Dictate problems from abacus math part of this week's homework.

1	2	3	4	5	6	7	8	9	10

11	12	13	14	15	16	17	18	19	20

21	22	23	24	25	26	27	28	29	30

SUDOKU

		6	4		3
3	2				1
4		3	2		
		2	3		4
6				3	2
2		5	1		

Fill in with numbers from 1 to 6. Make sure numbers do not repeat within each column, row or block.

MIRROR IMAGE

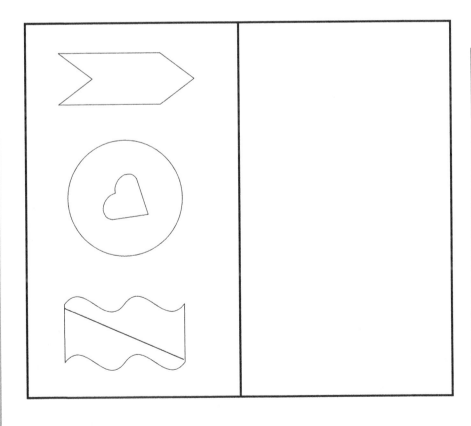

Draw the mirror images of the shapes on the other side of the line and color them. Use a mirror to see how the mirror image of each shape looks like.

Example:

Triangle | **its mirror image**

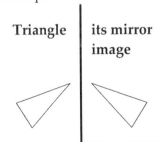

WEEK 14 – LESSON 13 – INTRODUCING +2 CONCEPT

LESSON 13 – PRACTICE WORK

$+ 2 = + 10 - 8$

Use Abacus

DAY 1 – MONDAY

TIME: _____min _____sec   Accuracy _____/32

1	2	3	4	5	6	7	8
28	49	69	38	49	84	79	59
02	12	12	21	40	25	12	22
20	- 20	20	22	22	42	20	21

14:1

1	2	3	4	5	6	7	8
74	43	49	48	39	58	79	98
22	45	02	12	42	12	12	21
23	22	- 31	50	24	- 40	60	32

14:2

1	2	3	4	5	6	7	8
48	58	58	77	38	33	45	89
22	22	22	42	42	42	53	22
24	52	32	29	44	74	20	88
22	22	- 12	32	22	02	12	62

14:3

1	2	3	4	5	6	7	8
99	88	54	75	65	144	254	385
22	62	95	78	65	34	43	114
33	19	12	- 20	35	212	121	22
22	82	43	22	87	125	32	89

14:4

DAY 2 – TUESDAY

TIME: _____ min _____ sec   Accuracy _____ /16

1	2	3	4	5	6	7	8	
48	78	59	88	66	29	29	89	14:5
42	52	54	22	28	22	45	22	
25	47	22	28	29	52	23	44	
37	- 34	27	12	- 11	25	23	98	
- 22	22	25	- 10	29	- 14	41	- 13	

1	2	3	4	5	6	7	8	
45	99	49	46	28	95	181	294	14:6
22	- 24	26	47	62	24	25	222	
12	72	84	22	24	13	47	45	
52	15	92	39	41	55	98	87	
24	23	- 11	- 41	- 32	64	- 310	12	

DAY 3 – WEDNESDAY

TIME: _____ min _____ sec   Accuracy _____ /16

1	2	3	4	5	6	7	8	
79	88	54	69	59	37	49	39	14:7
62	42	22	43	52	28	02	22	
22	- 20	22	28	35	27	15	- 40	
- 11	62	- 61	77	05	28	78	26	
- 32	23	29	- 14	- 20	23	11	13	

1	2	3	4	5	6	7	8	
48	62	69	66	87	97	59	175	14:8
12	85	23	26	47	24	222	62	
85	31	26	31	45	27	52	54	
07	72	27	25	12	28	45	22	
- 21	99	- 11	25	- 11	- 71	- 311	197	

DAY 4 – THURSDAY

TIME: _____ min _____ sec   Accuracy _____ /16 ☆

1	2	3	4	5	6	7	8
87	65	46	59	43	73	44	53
22	- 21	22	23	29	17	42	27
17	25	83	33	16	27	97	28
23	28	28	26	24	64	32	34
26	25	- 47	- 31	- 02	64	31	12

© SAI Speed Math Academy, USA   14:9

1	2	3	4	5	7	6	8
55	68	92	66	28	98	138	148
65	22	52	26	22	125	122	42
26	27	82	53	38	69	25	65
32	38	47	18	25	- 41	69	- 20
- 46	- 41	60	27	- 13	36	- 42	18

© SAI Speed Math Academy, USA   14:10

DAY 5 – FRIDAY

TIME: _____ min _____ sec   Accuracy _____ /16 ☆

1	2	3	4	5	6	7	8
66	74	49	66	55	66	79	77
62	32	34	57	- 41	- 13	42	52
32	29	27	55	68	29	54	29
27	87	28	72	22	54	- 62	26
59	32	16	- 40	- 03	56	22	97

© SAI Speed Math Academy, USA   14:11

1	2	3	4	5	6	7	8
29	59	47	45	17	154	109	134
24	25	24	24	29	212	184	25
64	26	28	43	38	89	122	22
26	85	55	22	46	76	82	- 130
- 33	96	- 32	- 34	24	45	64	94

© SAI Speed Math Academy, USA   14:12

LESSON 13 – MIND MATH PRACTICE WORK

DAY 1 – MONDAY

Accuracy _____/10

1	2	3	4	5	6	7	8	9	10
19	44	55	38	81	29	44	49	69	67
02	14	19	12	20	52	52	02	62	82
22	02	52	- 30	22	20	22	70	44	12

14:13

© SAI Speed Math Academy, USA

DAY 2 – TUESDAY

Accuracy _____/10

1	2	3	4	5	6	7	8	9	10
29	95	53	57	64	95	39	18	89	99
02	- 22	02	02	21	24	22	03	140	124
- 10	- 31	04	02	20	03	- 20	62	20	16
02	20	02	- 11	05	07	70	22	02	12

14:14

© SAI Speed Math Academy, USA

DAY 3 – WEDNESDAY

Accuracy _____/10

1	2	3	4	5	6	7	8	9	10
47	75	66	63	88	55	43	45	170	204
22	- 42	22	52	- 41	- 34	52	04	40	45
43	02	50	03	52	28	- 01	12	80	12
08	02	02	02	23	12	22	80	20	- 220

14:15

© SAI Speed Math Academy, USA

DAY 4 – THURSDAY

Accuracy _____/10

1	2	3	4	5	6	7	8	9	10
58	65	77	77	58	29	29	85	49	69
02	24	11	21	25	22	25	20	06	72
75	50	20	20	20	25	24	48	43	15
- 33	02	02	16	48	- 43	53	- 51	22	05

14:16

© SAI Speed Math Academy, USA

DAY 5 – FRIDAY

Accuracy _____/20 ☆

1	2	3	4	5	6	7	8	9	10
18	59	94	99	45	38	99	24	18	39
22	02	22	20	24	52	- 32	22	92	12
07	06	05	30	02	03	- 34	- 44	06	56
42	17	34	60	77	- 40	55	90	04	40
23	02	- 12	05	- 40	- 41	20	20	02	06

14:17

1	2	3	4	5	6	7	8	9	10
47	44	78	49	89	27	27	160	189	172
32	22	02	02	22	32	12	115	02	89
02	33	- 40	06	55	02	12	09	20	75
- 20	50	12	06	80	- 20	19	02	08	- 111
70	12	38	- 40	07	62	- 40	20	55	- 204

14:18

LESSON 13 – DICTATION

DICTATION: Dictation is when teacher or parent calls out a series of numbers and the child listens to the numbers and does the calculation in mind or on the abacus.

DO 6 PROBLEMS A DAY and write answers below.

Students: Try to calculate the dictated problems in mind.

Teachers: Dictate problems from abacus math part of this week's homework.

1	2	3	4	5	6	7	8	9	10

11	12	13	14	15	16	17	18	19	20

21	22	23	24	25	26	27	28	29	30

© SAI Speed Math Academy, USA

www.abacus-math.com

WORD BANK

Think of words that end with 'op', like in 'shop' or 'ow', like in 'crow' and write them on the line given. Use a dictionary to find more words and their meaning. Make a sentence using each of the words.

Shop _____ _____ _____

_____ _____ _____ _____

_____ _____ _____ _____

_____ _____ _____ _____

_____ _____ _____ _____

NUMBER BLOCK

		09		

Fill in the missing numbers

Use numbers 0 to 9 and fill in the empty cells.
Clues:
1. Rows add up to the total on the right.
2. Columns add up to the total at the bottom.
3. Diagonal cells up to the total shown in the top and bottom cells.
4. Numbers can repeat within a row or column.

1	4	3		14
2				15
	0		4	16
	0	9	1	13

13	12	17	16	15

		15		

0		5		15
			8	24
	2	4	0	12
0	1		1	05

11	11	16	18	12

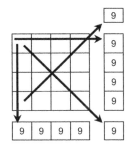

WEEK 15 – LESSON 14 – INTRODUCING +1 CONCEPT

This is a very important formula.

During Week 16 – Lesson 15 students will have to get help from this formula when used on the tens rod (+10 = +100 – 90) to complete all the big friends formula in specific situations. Example 99 + 02 = 101

So, please make sure that children are very clear in their understanding of this formula.

LESSON 14 – PRACTICE WORK

+ 1 = + 10 – 9

DAY 1 – MONDAY

TIME: _____ min _____ sec   Accuracy _____/32

1	2	3	4	5	6	7	8
28	29	39	49	49	84	98	59
61	11	11	11	01	11	11	31
01	- 40	90	80	70	16	11	10

15:1

1	2	3	4	5	6	7	8
55	99	89	48	94	49	77	84
35	14	31	11	12	42	52	11
10	37	30	51	48	14	21	19

15:2

1	2	3	4	5	6	7	8
18	19	59	18	65	49	96	47
11	31	21	11	24	11	64	- 14
19	49	15	- 20	01	- 20	19	26
14	11	17	41	11	99	71	91

15:3

1	2	3	4	5	6	7	8
17	29	18	28	309	263	189	357
17	21	24	37	51	235	21	- 214
15	14	55	33	- 20	11	39	116
11	- 31	15	11	10	11	11	11

15:4

DAY 2 – TUESDAY

TIME: _____ min _____ sec   Accuracy _____ /16

1	2	3	4	5	6	7	8
39	39	45	99	29	28	28	35
11	12	64	11	16	61	16	24
- 30	08	81	68	18	- 20	15	31
19	38	- 30	11	26	11	31	06
11	17	75	21	61	30	- 70	18

15:5

1	2	3	4	5	6	7	8
69	62	88	97	189	269	318	395
41	54	41	14	201	41	44	214
55	43	21	97	99	58	- 32	81
- 41	31	95	18	71	96	269	79
86	19	16	- 22	- 320	- 324	11	71

15:6

DAY 3 – WEDNESDAY

TIME: _____ min _____ sec   Accuracy _____ /16

1	2	3	4	5	6	7	8
49	37	39	76	27	62	24	26
41	18	51	22	24	- 20	33	24
11	15	19	10	17	15	24	09
15	28	71	34	01	18	18	11
16	18	58	22	11	05	11	- 30

15:7

1	2	3	4	5	6	7	8
49	15	38	55	536	149	249	195
11	47	27	17	- 403	101	111	114
18	37	24	99	96	14	57	51
14	13	51	38	54	86	45	35
- 22	36	60	11	223	- 120	- 440	119

15:8

DAY 4 – THURSDAY

TIME: _____ min _____ sec   Accuracy _____/16   ☆

1	2	3	4	5	6	7	8	
95	47	44	27	79	66	39	19	15:9
46	12	45	06	01	06	11	04	
78	71	01	29	08	51	08	49	
35	45	15	87	02	08	35	24	
91	79	38	11	10	19	- 93	15	

1	2	3	4	5	6	7	8	
59	96	37	29	149	269	189	127	15:10
25	47	15	34	111	101	41	43	
06	- 22	18	80	99	25	67	29	
- 80	38	89	16	101	86	13	51	
90	14	61	91	- 410	104	43	- 250	

DAY 5 – FRIDAY

TIME: _____ min _____ sec   Accuracy _____/16   ☆

1	2	3	4	5	6	7	8	
29	19	99	46	37	33	87	29	15:11
41	44	- 33	24	44	22	43	51	
88	18	- 22	08	08	- 11	28	- 40	
- 14	91	55	18	21	07	06	19	
27	- 61	11	18	36	09	50	91	

1	2	3	4	5	6	7	8	
19	17	25	37	215	369	188	526	15:12
11	13	25	17	27	13	422	- 101	
18	16	26	31	55	109	86	49	
12	14	16	09	115	118	- 202	17	
17	90	10	11	- 411	41	11	10	

LESSON 14 – MIND MATH PRACTICE WORK

DAY 1 – MONDAY   Accuracy _____/10 ⭐

1	2	3	4	5	6	7	8	9	10
44	09	38	94	58	75	39	88	69	65
11	11	11	01	91	19	11	11	42	80
11	10	11	10	01	11	- 50	15	44	16

15:13

DAY 2 – TUESDAY   Accuracy _____/10 ⭐

1	2	3	4	5	6	7	8	9	10
19	24	54	19	05	84	95	54	98	94
09	25	05	58	25	15	17	56	11	10
81	11	- 10	02	29	15	50	19	11	51
01	- 40	61	51	01	- 03	05	11	- 20	- 33

15:14

DAY 3 – WEDNESDAY   Accuracy _____/10 ⭐

1	2	3	4	5	6	7	8	9	10
41	36	23	47	54	46	79	49	86	95
15	60	75	17	55	35	01	08	- 14	17
41	56	11	- 53	11	15	05	33	27	35
15	- 51	01	15	07	10	08	- 40	31	10

15:15

DAY 4 – THURSDAY   Accuracy _____/10 ⭐

1	2	3	4	5	6	7	8	9	10
85	74	85	77	99	76	186	111	197	55
09	08	05	04	12	23	07	66	13	106
15	57	10	- 50	11	11	15	22	45	38
01	11	23	23	- 02	- 110	42	10	- 211	21

15:16

Accuracy _____/20 ☆

1	2	3	4	5	6	7	8	9	10
09	67	44	75	39	73	58	72	53	55
01	25	89	- 42	22	05	25	33	27	- 11
44	17	66	65	55	71	26	44	14	22
25	01	50	14	06	11	81	21	01	33
01	16	01	- 12	33	- 20	10	- 70	16	11

15:17
© SAI Speed Math Academy, USA

1	2	3	4	5	6	7	8	9	10
48	79	24	77	67	45	44	149	599	349
42	43	51	17	30	24	17	60	- 104	- 220
39	47	16	01	12	23	28	- 207	10	11
24	01	10	10	31	15	51	93	- 302	110
- 53	- 60	21	- 01	- 40	43	- 20	17	- 203	- 240

15:18
© SAI Speed Math Academy, USA

LESSON 14 – DICTATION

DICTATION: Dictation is when teacher or parent calls out a series of numbers and the child listens to the numbers and does the calculation in mind or on the abacus.

DO 6 PROBLEMS A DAY and write answers below.

Students: Try to calculate the dictated problems in mind.

Teachers: Dictate problems from abacus math part of this week's homework.

1	2	3	4	5	6	7	8	9	10

11	12	13	14	15	16	17	18	19	20

21	22	23	24	25	26	27	28	29	30

DRAW AND COLOR A PICTURE OF YOUR FAVORITE WILD ANIMAL

NUMBER GAME

RULE: 1) Using ONLY the given numbers answer the questions.

   2) Use the numbers only once.

Also, write their names next to it in words.

Example: Use 2, 6.

Largest = 62 -- sixty two

Smallest = 26 -- twenty six

Your numbers to use are 4, and 9. Write the number and its name in words.

Largest number you can make: _____

Smallest number you can make: _____

Your numbers to use are 3, 1, and 8. Write the number and its name in words.

Largest number you can make: _____

Smallest number you can make: _____

Your numbers to use are 4, 9, and 5. Write the number and its name in words.

Largest number you can make: _____

Smallest number you can make: _____

CHALLENGE: Your numbers to use are 4, 7, 1, and 2. Write the number and its name in words.

Think of place values.

Largest number you can make: _____

_____

Smallest number you can make: _____

_____

WEEK 16 – LESSON 15 – INTRODUCING REGROUPING OR CARRY-OVER TO HUNDREDS ROD

CONCEPTS OF THE WEEK – REGROUPING OR CARRYOVER TO THE HUNDREDS ROD

TO ADD = ADD 10, LESS BIG FRIEND

TO ADD 10 = If you do not have enough beads to +10 in a formula

USE = +10 = +100 − 90

For detailed instructions please refer:
Abacus Mind Math Instruction Book Level 2: Step by Step Guide to Excel at Mind Math with Soroban, a Japanese Abacus **ISBN 978-1-941589-03-8**

+9 = +10 − 1	+4 = +10 − 6
+8 = +10 − 2	+3 = +10 − 7
+7 = +10 − 3	+2 = +10 − 8
+6 = +10 − 4	+1 = +10 − 9
+5 = +10 − 5	+10 = +100 − 90

What do you need to succeed?

Passion, patience, practice, tenacity and commitment.

www.abacus-math.com

PRACTICE PROBLEMS:

We have given a few problems in the rows below where students have had the most difficulty.

1	2	3	4	5	6	7	8	9	10	
99 01	99 11	89 01	89 11	99 02	99 12	89 12	89 02	99 03	99 13	16:S:5 © SAI Speed Math Academy, USA

1	2	3	4	5	6	7	8	9	10	
89 03	89 13	99 04	99 14	89 04	89 14	99 05	99 15	89 15	89 05	16:S:6 © SAI Speed Math Academy, USA

1	2	3	4	5	6	7	8	9	10	
99 06	99 16	89 06	89 16	99 07	99 17	89 17	89 07	99 08	99 18	16:S:7 © SAI Speed Math Academy, USA

1	2	3	4	5	6	7	8	9	10	
89 08	89 18	99 09	99 19	89 19	89 09	95 09	95 19	85 09	85 19	16:S:8 © SAI Speed Math Academy, USA

1	2	3	4	5	6	7	8	9	10	
96 08	95 18	86 18	85 08	95 07	96 17	87 07	85 17	96 06	88 16	16:S:9 © SAI Speed Math Academy, USA

1	2	3	4	5	6	7	8	9	10	
386 118	405 98	246 258	435 168	395 207	296 117	187 316	485 117	206 296	488 116	16:S:10 © SAI Speed Math Academy, USA

LESSON 15 – PRACTICE WORK

Use Abacus

DAY 1 – MONDAY

TIME: _____ min _____ sec   Accuracy _____ /32

1	2	3	4	5	6	7	8	
36	25	14	24	17	44	13	81	16:1
63	74	75	65	82	55	76	08	
01	11	01	11	02	12	12	02	

1	2	3	4	5	6	7	8	
63	46	44	29	99	99	79	59	16:2
35	51	44	63	03	13	13	33	
03	13	03	08	99	09	08	19	

1	2	3	4	5	6	7	8	
55	34	85	67	28	95	37	42	16:3
- 21	56	25	48	67	09	15	55	
65	56	87	92	06	09	39	06	
89	89	04	07	60	42	- 61	23	

1	2	3	4	5	6	7	8	
72	54	86	354	442	293	199	375	16:4
29	37	- 15	298	256	164	105	124	
96	08	22	- 220	006	45	295	107	
04	01	21	- 401	- 304	- 100	01	- 302	

www.abacus-math.com

DAY 2 – TUESDAY

TIME: _____ min _____ sec   Accuracy _____ /16

1	2	3	4	5	6	7	8	
29	35	65	77	99	21	27	33	16:5
70	63	24	27	05	75	50	56	
04	14	04	87	97	15	15	15	

1	2	3	4	5	6	7	8	
14	64	26	37	99	159	194	555	16:6
57	59	45	25	- 67	241	07	- 241	
35	65	35	23	57	75	65	72	
78	- 44	89	09	13	- 330	235	118	
- 21	21	09	- 94	98	357	- 401	- 404	

DAY 3 – WEDNESDAY

TIME: _____ min _____ sec   Accuracy _____ /16

1	2	3	4	5	6	7	8	
45	62	23	47	34	22	16	54	16:7
50	35	64	40	61	77	70	33	
06	16	06	16	07	17	17	07	

1	2	3	4	5	6	7	8	
44	39	67	45	44	25	274	195	16:8
55	87	38	24	17	46	255	107	
- 76	55	65	12	28	14	89	175	
59	07	56	13	- 42	- 30	- 514	175	
68	12	74	15	55	49	398	- 420	

DAY 4 – THURSDAY

TIME: _____min _____sec   Accuracy _____/16

1	2	3	4	5	6	7	8
75	45	23	17	99	16	89	18
- 11	45	22	05	02	15	11	45
32	06	51	45	97	67	95	15
04	08	09	- 16	- 54	07	- 24	- 77

16:9

1	2	3	4	5	6	7	8
26	33	14	14	19	299	196	148
83	28	37	19	16	89	105	257
92	19	29	18	25	- 44	142	- 201
13	18	07	14	39	55	134	91
25	- 31	- 33	37	22	102	- 246	08

16:10

DAY 5 – FRIDAY

TIME: _____min _____sec   Accuracy _____/16

1	2	3	4	5	6	7	8
77	33	55	19	43	79	55	91
25	66	37	81	48	16	- 14	46
07	09	04	09	09	08	52	15
18	55	- 65	44	16	- 03	07	58

16:11

1	2	3	4	5	6	7	8
55	33	65	42	25	286	126	135
45	22	- 24	16	76	143	435	126
96	44	55	15	45	172	96	109
16	79	14	19	- 33	- 400	83	- 30
19	66	32	- 81	68	99	71	- 210

16:12

LESSON 15 – MIND MATH PRACTICE WORK

Visualize

DAY 1 – MONDAY

Accuracy _____/10 ⭐

1	2	3	4	5	6	7	8	9	10	
99	99	99	99	99	99	99	99	99	99	16:13
01	02	03	04	05	06	07	08	09	11	
05	45	25	05	05	05	05	05	29	40	

DAY 2 – TUESDAY

Accuracy _____/10 ⭐

1	2	3	4	5	6	7	8	9	10	
98	97	96	95	94	93	82	85	75	76	16:14
02	03	04	05	06	07	18	19	27	18	
43	72	38	28	22	16	14	44	42	06	

DAY 3 – WEDNESDAY

Accuracy _____/10 ⭐

1	2	3	4	5	6	7	8	9	10	
97	98	41	36	85	74	75	47	17	199	16:15
07	06	55	55	- 41	55	61	05	18	104	
08	29	03	09	46	92	45	45	14	52	
- 12	05	55	57	78	- 11	- 51	05	15	- 201	

DAY 4 – THURSDAY

Accuracy _____/10 ⭐

1	2	3	4	5	6	7	8	9	10	
31	11	41	24	81	45	19	32	188	455	16:16
17	45	50	16	05	45	76	64	12	47	
21	49	05	55	08	24	09	04	45	33	
07	08	08	17	06	34	24	05	09	17	

DAY 5 – FRIDAY

1	2	3	4	5	6	7	8	9	10
46	96	45	43	92	66	44	27	95	94
13	04	55	52	07	30	16	25	09	05
05	32	03	55	01	- 03	39	23	98	06
- 52	76	08	65	48	09	02	25	48	- 04

16:17 © SAI Speed Math Academy, USA

1	2	3	4	5	6	7	8	9	10
54	19	05	86	95	54	298	198	599	169
41	58	25	17	07	56	107	119	- 104	16
06	22	19	05	20	57	92	78	07	07
55	03	16	- 03	05	- 26	104	109	- 202	209

16:18 © SAI Speed Math Academy, USA

LESSON 15– DICTATION

DICTATION: Dictation is when teacher or parent calls out a series of numbers and the child listens to the numbers and does the calculation in mind or on the abacus.

DO 6 PROBLEMS A DAY and write answers below.

Students: Try to calculate the dictated problems in mind.

Teachers: Dictate problems from mind math part of this week's homework.

1	2	3	4	5	6	7	8	9	10

11	12	13	14	15	16	17	18	19	20

21	22	23	24	25	26	27	28	29	30

UNSCRAMBLE

First letter in each name is in the right place, so don't change.

BKALSALTEB _____   Shoot into the hoop

SRCCEO _____   Rule of the game: cannot pick ball with hands

BBELSAAL _____   Touch base

SMNWMGII _____   Race in water

FENIGCN _____   Sword fight

SIGINPPK _____   Use a rope

POOL _____   Ride a horse while playing

FURIEG SAIGTNK _____   Glide on ice

GANSISCYMT _____   Perfect '10' score possible

WORD MORPHING

Change the first word into the last word. Change only one letter at a time.	YOU CAN CHANGE ONLY ONE LETTER EACH STEP. YOU CANNOT CHANGE SAME LETTER SECOND TIME.
Example: CAT to FUN	FIG _____ _____ BEE
CAT CAT	SAW _____ _____ POD
____ FAT	CRY _____ _____ FLU
____ FAN	COT _____ _____ PAN
FUN FUN	

WEEK 17 – SKILL BUILDING

WEEK 17 – PRACTICE WORK

Use Abacus

DAY 1 – MONDAY

TIME: _____min _____sec   Accuracy _____/16

1	2	3	4	5	6	7	8
14	52	38	39	96	95	98	25
24	46	15	87	08	09	06	46
- 22	04	44	55	48	65	25	14
34	66	08	07	45	32	21	- 31
44	- 32	- 01	- 34	13	22	55	- 23

17:1

1	2	3	4	5	6	7	8
56	88	66	98	149	295	443	157
57	22	28	87	151	17	12	38
82	28	29	76	89	275	45	55
08	19	- 11	65	- 214	- 441	57	- 130
53	46	29	74	228	58	- 316	380

17:2

SHAPE PUZZLE

Find out what each shape is worth.

Suggestion: Take as many numbers of beans, blocks or coins as the right side of the equation shows and share them on the shapes to the left side of the equation.

$$☀ + ☀ + ☀ + ☀ + ☀ = 15$$

$$◯ - ☀ = 02$$

$$◯ + ◯ + ☀ + ∪ = 17$$

$$☀ + ◯ + ☀ - ∪ - ⬔ = 02$$

DAY 2 – TUESDAY

TIME: _____ min _____ sec   Accuracy _____ /16 ☆

1	2	3	4	5	6	7	8
36	34	55	65	88	46	26	69
45	55	15	22	- 42	23	16	15
38	16	26	87	59	25	44	19
65	78	36	55	76	79	- 33	45
- 34	- 63	49	29	34	- 32	71	54

17:3

1	2	3	4	5	6	7	8
15	32	25	286	96	398	232	165
25	26	75	143	105	147	55	289
35	05	45	62	42	- 201	89	41
45	29	- 33	66	134	15	128	107
55	- 92	68	- 211	- 246	91	- 404	- 300

17:4

DAY 3 – WEDNESDAY

TIME: _____ min _____ sec   Accuracy _____ /16 ☆

1	2	3	4	5	6	7	8
87	58	78	85	32	44	34	98
35	86	35	17	42	35	24	02
69	27	36	25	52	26	47	17
15	26	34	08	62	17	49	08
- 04	28	43	44	- 73	- 22	- 31	79

17:5

1	2	3	4	5	6	7	8
14	41	14	133	555	199	295	188
26	22	57	122	- 214	65	105	161
35	33	35	144	55	39	178	189
45	25	78	101	14	16	136	31
19	47	- 21	26	- 310	187	- 404	- 333

17:6

DAY 4 – THURSDAY

TIME: _____min _____sec   Accuracy _____/16 ☆

1	2	3	4	5	6	7	8	
29	59	65	46	45	24	19	65	
66	46	- 21	28	07	25	18	29	
25	17	73	37	73	26	17	09	17:7
34	38	28	28	79	27	16	88	
21	- 20	19	46	15	28	15	- 71	

1	2	3	4	5	6	7	8	
79	44	62	192	235	194	179	55	
22	11	94	35	254	154	72	98	
34	33	97	46	14	113	37	175	17:8
54	- 25	53	86	- 300	55	11	155	
11	- 31	45	143	47	- 314	191	22	

DAY 5 – FRIDAY

TIME: _____min _____sec   Accuracy _____/16 ☆

1	2	3	4	5	6	7	8	
67	39	44	55	64	26	37	29	
87	24	58	45	59	45	25	45	
92	37	26	96	65	35	23	23	17:9
64	96	31	16	- 44	89	09	23	
46	- 34	- 46	19	21	- 61	- 94	44	

1	2	3	4	5	6	7	8	
89	58	39	193	192	298	279	576	
31	77	42	112	105	54	262	- 132	
26	11	06	45	46	45	226	76	17:10
22	05	14	57	- 140	101	- 311	89	
33	49	29	- 201	77	11	44	41	

WEEK 17 – MIND MATH PRACTICE WORK

Visualize

DAY 1 – MONDAY

Accuracy _____/10

1	2	3	4	5	6	7	8	9	10
35	27	18	54	75	35	31	41	140	442
56	14	57	51	09	56	20	15	15	155
07	07	05	58	15	05	15	09	150	- 306
65	13	26	60	10	08	38	- 11	07	- 100
- 40	37	44	- 23	43	- 04	11	- 11	- 101	09

17:11

DAY 2 – TUESDAY

Accuracy _____/10

1	2	3	4	5	6	7	8	9	10
14	39	77	49	89	28	27	16	115	544
35	21	22	12	02	53	34	26	37	- 420
01	06	11	06	- 70	07	08	60	- 41	05
- 20	07	17	33	07	65	04	55	25	70
09	- 31	06	50	22	- 13	- 22	- 24	14	301

17:12

DAY 3 – WEDNESDAY

Accuracy _____/10

1	2	3	4	5	6	7	8	9	10
48	79	24	97	67	45	44	53	349	272
42	43	51	07	38	24	17	27	02	233
24	47	26	35	65	12	28	15	94	84
23	22	65	36	56	13	- 42	- 51	39	93
- 27	- 61	- 21	35	08	15	- 26	16	- 243	- 331

17:13

DAY 4 – THURSDAY

Accuracy _____/10

1	2	3	4	5	6	7	8	9	10
49	37	39	76	69	62	88	97	189	269
41	18	51	22	41	54	41	14	201	42
11	15	19	10	55	43	41	97	09	58
15	28	71	34	- 41	31	- 60	48	105	13
16	18	58	22	86	19	95	- 22	- 304	44

17:14 © SAI Speed Math Academy, USA

DAY 5 – FRIDAY

Accuracy _____/20 ☆

1	2	3	4	5	6	7	8	9	10
44	39	33	45	29	11	26	79	397	395
08	55	34	07	28	88	33	05	65	107
37	44	35	38	17	- 76	42	27	85	- 400
21	29	36	17	- 41	55	15	55	56	96
17	19	- 38	99	67	23	- 12	86	- 301	03

17:15 © SAI Speed Math Academy, USA

1	2	3	4	5	6	7	8	9	10
36	72	24	26	29	13	48	47	536	149
15	- 30	33	24	11	47	07	23	- 403	141
17	15	24	09	18	37	34	99	96	14
31	48	17	11	42	13	12	- 43	54	66
11	95	06	- 30	11	36	60	- 24	223	08

17:16 © SAI Speed Math Academy, USA

WORD MORPHING

Change the first word into the last word. Change only one letter at a time.

Example: CAT to FUN

CAT	CAT
___	FAT
___	FAN
FUN	FUN

YOU CAN CHANGE ONLY ONE LETTER EACH STEP. YOU CANNOT CHANGE SAME LETTER SECOND TIME.

ZORO _____ _____ _____ HEED

MAKE _____ _____ _____ PINT

www.abacus-math.com

WEEK 17 – DICTATION

DICTATION: Dictation is when teacher or parent calls out a series of numbers and the child listens to the numbers and does the calculation in mind or on the abacus.

DO 6 PROBLEMS A DAY and write answers below.

Students: Try to calculate the dictated problems in mind.

Teachers: Dictate problems from abacus math part of this week's homework.

1	2	3	4	5	6	7	8	9	10

11	12	13	14	15	16	17	18	19	20

21	22	23	24	25	26	27	28	29	30

WORD BANK

Think of words that end with 'ap', like in 'gap' or 'eep', like in 'weep' and write them on the line given. Use a dictionary to find more words and their meaning. Make a sentence using each of the words.

Weep _____ _____ _____ _____

_____ _____ _____ _____

_____ _____ _____ _____

_____ _____ _____ _____

WEEK 18 – SKILL BUILDING

WEEK 18 – PRACTICE WORK

Use Abacus

DAY 1 – MONDAY TIME: _____min _____sec Accuracy _____/16 ⭐

1	2	3	4	5	6	7	8	
47	15	29	25	41	56	52	78	
84	95	54	79	12	76	85	64	
19	58	94	51	38	17	98	85	18:1
- 20	21	- 23	49	59	71	66	75	
46	- 64	85	43	86	25	78	63	
- 62	- 23	17	98	67	58	66	- 45	

© SAI Speed Math Academy, USA

1	2	3	4	5	6	7	8	
10	27	30	157	379	96	16	231	
31	80	82	180	18	237	117	53	
94	94	87	144	- 61	227	55	91	18:2
37	67	60	154	166	94	165	29	
91	86	31	86	15	43	92	41	
14	10	30	98	37	04	58	16	

© SAI Speed Math Academy, USA

RIDDLE TIME

1. What belongs to you, but others use it a lot?

2. What happens when you drop your white hat in the Dead Sea?

3. Who has a head and a tail but no body?

www.abacus-math.com

1	2	3	4	5	6	7	8	
15	29	80	74	65	58	75	23	
69	20	91	28	24	56	26	14	
40	70	26	44	81	46	24	12	
21	24	94	28	72	35	29	50	18:3
40	34	28	15	67	- 43	71	26	
47	54	83	- 77	88	96	75	35	

© SAI Speed Math Academy, USA

1	2	3	4	5	6	7	8	
34	54	95	82	369	366	292	769	
93	14	17	143	53	38	24	- 427	
16	82	89	85	42	91	29	55	
25	95	58	190	77	55	109	07	18:4
91	40	- 19	75	- 410	- 320	- 30	48	
44	33	25	- 112	369	270	- 424	- 430	

© SAI Speed Math Academy, USA

WORD MORPHING

Change the first word into the last word. You can change only one letter each step. You cannot change same letter second time.

Example: CAT to FUN		
CAT	CAT
	↓
____	FAT
	↓
____	FAN
	↓
FUN	FUN

FAN _____ _____ BIT

SEE _____ _____ BAT

BIG _____ _____ SAT

BUD _____ _____ SAY

TIME: _____min _____sec   Accuracy _____/16

1	2	3	4	5	6	7	8
73	57	31	61	48	58	72	24
64	77	16	39	43	60	57	81
56	13	15	45	27	49	96	91
67	53	51	57	37	- 25	47	18
40	16	52	67	21	57	25	71
49	98	18	- 48	25	01	56	- 63

18:5

1	2	3	4	5	6	7	8
97	49	63	568	112	271	555	389
15	77	59	42	111	39	98	111
74	48	12	88	158	47	22	67
- 33	- 12	56	103	167	- 334	76	72
16	- 30	87	95	113	55	24	15
83	22	- 46	04	145	75	- 461	- 654

18:6

MIRROR IMAGE

Draw mirror image of the picture on the other side of the line next to it.

TIME: _____min _____sec   Accuracy _____/16 ☆

1	2	3	4	5	6	7	8	
93	36	97	57	44	87	45	31	
68	15	12	38	49	16	93	83	
32	76	36	80	54	49	27	24	
74	37	98	14	- 13	65	87	11	18:7
52	28	49	31	11	69	73	53	
24	64	28	32	16	- 22	84	60	

1	2	3	4	5	6	7	8	
68	74	44	236	247	396	87	549	
65	73	15	15	254	52	445	52	
21	87	41	57	90	55	34	55	
91	26	88	14	85	82	- 201	- 214	18:8
51	34	- 44	46	- 432	- 401	33	16	
13	36	- 14	182	- 144	66	111	46	

WORD LIST

List words with five letters or more that **starts** with a 'T' as in 'Tiger" or with 'H' as in 'History'. Write a story and try to use at least 5 words from the list in your story.

—————— —————— —————— ——————

—————— —————— —————— ——————

—————— —————— —————— ——————

—————— —————— —————— ——————

—————— —————— —————— ——————

TIME: _____min _____sec   Accuracy _____/16

1	2	3	4	5	6	7	8	
79	56	51	52	41	19	83	13	
34	82	87	44	74	99	96	84	
87	61	69	- 72	66	36	32	17	
76	46	65	65	52	11	34	58	18:9
83	57	35	11	16	- 24	24	51	
52	35	45	98	11	15	51	66	

© SAI Speed Math Academy, USA

1	2	3	4	5	6	7	8	
33	22	18	112	188	140	316	101	
81	53	12	75	386	67	54	443	
31	11	38	266	- 241	33	95	92	
77	20	- 41	12	55	10	- 61	19	18:10
45	88	79	87	115	17	98	- 402	
- 36	11	44	- 542	- 203	- 247	49	296	

© SAI Speed Math Academy, USA

MIRROR IMAGE

Draw mirror image of the picture on the other side of the line next to it.

WEEK 18 – MIND MATH PRACTICE WORK

DAY 1 – MONDAY

Accuracy _____/10 ☆

1	2	3	4	5	6	7	8	9	10
73	88	91	37	79	14	19	99	576	758
29	14	52	37	83	19	16	89	- 463	- 120
66	35	42	15	41	28	25	- 44	97	- 303
32	08	08	67	55	13	36	- 21	85	- 104
88	- 32	25	- 13	- 14	17	- 22	37	- 232	69

18:11 © SAI Speed Math Academy, USA

DAY 2 – TUESDAY

Accuracy _____/10 ☆

1	2	3	4	5	6	7	8	9	10
95	47	44	24	09	66	39	19	259	189
46	42	45	06	01	06	11	04	25	43
78	71	01	29	08	51	08	49	111	54
80	45	17	11	02	42	35	24	- 80	- 13
12	07	88	29	90	39	- 22	- 96	135	- 273

18:12 © SAI Speed Math Academy, USA

DAY 3 – WEDNESDAY

Accuracy _____/10 ☆

1	2	3	4	5	6	7	8	9	10
26	58	79	50	85	84	54	67	98	66
86	52	22	40	68	35	58	37	21	92
14	59	19	83	57	52	31	08	49	96
86	31	79	43	51	98	62	15	83	79
14	46	01	14	58	35	45	75	13	29

18:13 © SAI Speed Math Academy, USA

DAY 4 – THURSDAY

1	2	3	4	5	6	7	8	9	10
26	55	24	97	96	95	98	53	198	190
42	96	51	07	08	09	06	27	03	109
41	28	26	35	48	65	25	15	56	02
55	- 46	65	36	45	65	21	- 51	85	84
- 44	22	- 21	35	49	- 22	- 10	16	- 341	115

18:14

DAY 5 – FRIDAY

Accuracy _____/20

1	2	3	4	5	6	7	8	9	10
14	41	14	33	55	79	44	62	392	235
26	22	57	22	- 14	21	11	98	35	256
35	33	35	44	55	34	33	07	96	167
45	25	78	79	14	54	- 25	- 53	55	- 313
19	47	- 21	66	32	12	- 31	- 13	- 108	28

18:15

1	2	3	4	5	6	7	8	9	10
79	59	65	46	44	11	55	26	999	478
83	46	- 21	28	55	22	- 11	89	- 63	29
41	17	73	37	66	33	22	87	- 300	- 103
55	38	28	28	77	44	28	75	- 313	54
- 14	- 20	19	46	88	99	31	- 37	- 200	60

18:16

MISSING NUMBERS   17

Find out the missing number and write on top. Example   14, 15, 16, 18, 19, 20, 21, 22, 23, 24
Take a close look, there is more than just one number missing!

325, 326, 327, 328, 329, 330, 332, 333, 335, 336, 337, 338, 340, 341, 342, 344, 345, 347, 349,

351, 353, 354, 355, 357, 358, 359, 361, 362, 363, 364, 365, 367, 368, 369, 370, 371, 372, 374,

375, 376, 378, 379, 380, 382, 384, 385, 386, 387, 388, 389, 391, 392, 393, 395, 396, 397, 399,

401, 402, 403, 405, 406, 408, 409, 411, 412, 414, 416, 417, 418, 420, 421, 423, 424, 426, 427

WEEK 18 – DICTATION

DICTATION: Dictation is when teacher or parent calls out a series of numbers and the child listens to the numbers and does the calculation in mind or on the abacus.

DO 6 PROBLEMS A DAY and write answers below.
Students: Try to calculate the dictated problems in mind.
Teachers: Dictate problems from abacus math part of this week's homework.

1	2	3	4	5	6	7	8	9	10

11	12	13	14	15	16	17	18	19	20

21	22	23	24	25	26	27	28	29	30

SEPARATE SHAPES

Use 4 straight lines to separate the ribbons into its' own space.

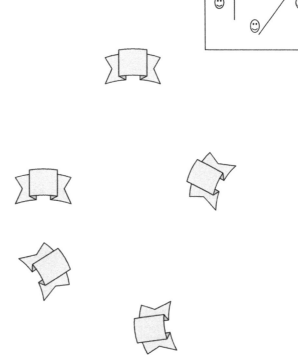

For Example:

WEEK 19 – SKILL BUILDING

WEEK 19 – PRACTICE WORK

Use Abacus

DAY 1 – MONDAY

TIME: _____min _____sec Accuracy _____/16

1	2	3	4	5	6	7	8	
53	25	24	56	49	92	86	41	
93	26	35	26	46	70	16	16	
21	27	63	28	81	57	35	32	
43	28	59	83	- 42	61	52	76	19:1
73	17	27	38	57	84	11	94	
62	15	44	57	37	41	34	63	

1	2	3	4	5	6	7	8	
934	136	759	654	569	804	595	188	
- 420	290	- 657	194	391	74	- 164	288	
- 101	522	144	- 315	- 730	- 843	395	36	
33	- 704	58	- 311	19	232	- 822	- 400	19:2
55	51	51	29	52	132	91	55	
- 301	207	- 354	138	91	101	- 95	387	

RIDDLE TIME

1. I am not alive but I move around. I don't breathe but I need air. I don't like water because it destroys me. Hmmmmmm..... Who am I?

2. What type of tie does Mr. Ghost like to wear to formal events?

3. A man had a pile of wood next to him. Wood was not straight, crooked or curled. What type of wood was it?

TIME: _____min _____sec   Accuracy _____/16 ☆

1	2	3	4	5	6	7	8	
16	97	56	59	93	73	32	36	
82	96	14	39	71	22	88	53	
14	68	59	29	25	94	98	44	19:3
82	52	61	63	25	13	13	45	
58	87	83	23	64	82	26	34	
96	87	64	86	16	19	45	11	

1	2	3	4	5	6	7	8	
590	457	744	143	697	423	383	118	
47	223	38	785	- 433	32	- 201	584	
112	175	- 562	- 307	81	168	405	- 601	19:4
151	97	55	- 401	12	- 321	- 554	52	
- 400	- 710	14	36	44	92	22	746	
- 100	115	14	295	- 401	11	55	01	

WORD MORPHING

Change the first word into the last word. You can change only one letter each step. You cannot change same letter second time.

PIKE _____ _____ _____ MALL

KIDS _____ _____ _____ MUST

1	2	3	4	5	6	7	8
95	18	60	23	65	21	37	79
28	29	26	84	83	85	77	23
36	31	52	93	- 28	39	14	70
77	88	74	19	16	55	12	77
42	66	89	31	58	76	76	17
62	60	19	- 40	51	24	67	41

19:5

1	2	3	4	5	6	7	8
631	442	166	186	305	52	231	152
194	418	133	318	382	587	633	693
99	- 620	132	41	- 432	186	- 724	35
- 724	16	51	- 130	272	- 705	38	- 770
66	- 24	- 40	82	71	31	- 42	22
185	45	256	103	- 598	23	66	42

19:6

MIRROR IMAGE

Draw mirror image of the picture on the other side of the line next to it.

DAY 4 – THURSDAY

TIME: _____ min _____ sec Accuracy _____ /16

1	2	3	4	5	6	7	8	
27	37	84	75	34	14	43	55	
91	70	79	45	57	23	79	96	
88	95	90	57	42	34	65	84	19:7
28	15	58	- 63	48	61	- 42	78	
83	43	96	71	74	27	10	52	
- 14	45	42	19	- 21	11	- 12	- 42	

1	2	3	4	5	6	7	8	
152	186	39	255	111	868	201	84	
195	457	375	158	320	- 542	640	144	
172	- 223	213	43	149	79	85	232	19:8
94	75	- 602	- 431	- 280	41	- 803	- 410	
48	18	- 12	56	37	51	123	- 10	
- 661	- 111	358	- 81	14	115	123	60	

MISSING NUMBERS

Fill in the missing numbers

Use numbers 0 to 9 and fill in the empty cells.
Clues:
1. Rows add up to the total on the right.
2. Columns add up to the total at the bottom.
3. Diagonal cells up to the total shown in the top and bottom cells.
4. Numbers can repeat within a row or column.

Left puzzle:

				13
	5	5	0	**14**
		1		**19**
1	7	1		**16**
5	4			**17**
14	**21**	**10**	**21**	**15**

Right puzzle:

				15
	2	4		**11**
		5	6	**25**
5			4	**24**
2	3		5	**19**
20	**19**	**25**	**15**	**23**

DAY 5 – FRIDAY

1	2	3	4	5	6	7	8
68	91	54	65	42	26	78	56
19	26	27	46	68	43	85	98
65	72	86	68	26	17	82	74
83	34	65	85	79	84	49	31
63	18	23	43	88	36	57	- 46
25	28	- 11	45	48	24	36	92

© SAI Speed Math Academy, USA · 19:9

1	2	3	4	5	6	7	8
58	134	263	310	250	307	228	371
41	392	228	197	255	262	254	31
151	13	144	- 104	- 201	- 147	17	160
19	- 407	- 601	41	65	72	123	94
15	26	22	55	42	146	- 311	- 634
221	44	- 15	55	- 411	110	54	- 22

© SAI Speed Math Academy, USA · 19:10

MIRROR IMAGE

Draw mirror image of the picture on the other side of the line next to it.

WEEK 19 – MIND MATH PRACTICE WORK

DAY 1 – MONDAY

Accuracy _____/10 ☆

1	2	3	4	5	6	7	8	9	10
45	65	94	19	32	44	34	94	357	183
07	29	06	65	42	35	25	08	82	23
76	09	87	18	52	26	47	65	56	93
29	88	04	65	62	17	69	- 23	- 41	- 72
- 15	- 71	- 70	- 43	- 73	- 22	- 31	- 31	90	99

19:11

DAY 2 – TUESDAY

Accuracy _____/10 ☆

1	2	3	4	5	6	7	8	9	10
85	58	78	87	43	29	95	88	199	295
07	86	35	45	53	54	08	12	04	105
05	27	36	69	13	- 41	43	17	39	178
08	26	43	15	11	54	22	08	16	36
44	28	43	- 13	33	16	- 55	19	- 27	- 204

19:12

DAY 3 – WEDNESDAY

Accuracy _____/10 ☆

1	2	3	4	5	6	7	8	9	10
39	44	55	64	26	37	29	89	279	576
24	58	45	59	45	25	45	31	260	- 132
37	26	96	65	35	23	23	26	62	76
96	31	16	- 44	89	09	23	22	- 401	75
- 34	- 46	19	21	- 61	- 94	44	- 24	- 200	106

19:13

DAY 4 – THURSDAY

Accuracy _____/10 ☆

1	2	3	4	5	6	7	8	9	10
24	19	33	14	52	38	26	254	227	262
25	12	34	24	46	15	33	95	465	135
26	16	35	- 22	04	44	42	- 08	- 351	07
27	19	36	34	66	08	15	55	56	96
28	18	- 38	44	- 32	- 01	- 12	06	106	- 300

19:14

DAY 5 – FRIDAY

Accuracy _____/20 ☆

1	2	3	4	5	6	7	8	9	10
57	68	30	40	56	90	28	199	185	216
22	41	80	31	80	43	84	17	98	73
37	81	36	98	10	31	27	102	- 230	61
58	60	73	33	- 42	60	13	06	46	- 210
- 30	30	68	52	80	44	73	47	403	80

19:15

1	2	3	4	5	6	7	8	9	10
80	29	36	71	23	58	83	183	206	169
27	16	86	57	76	64	46	81	24	10
84	70	58	23	21	57	20	19	115	135
42	82	75	- 11	09	- 78	61	54	45	36
95	- 03	- 23	20	26	40	99	160	26	33
18	- 94	57	- 40	- 33	35	- 08	15	- 405	44

19:16

WEEK 19 – DICTATION

DICTATION: Dictation is when teacher or parent calls out a series of numbers and the child listens to the numbers and does the calculation in mind or on the abacus.

DO 6 PROBLEMS A DAY and write answers below.
Students: Try to calculate the dictated problems in mind.
Teachers: Dictate problems from abacus math part of this week's homework.

1	2	3	4	5	6	7	8	9	10

11	12	13	14	15	16	17	18	19	20

21	22	23	24	25	26	27	28	29	30

SHAPE PUZZLE

Find out what each shape is worth.

Clue: Study 2nd equation and see how the facts given here can be used to solve other equations.

$$\text{star} + \text{circle} + \text{moon} = 13$$

$$\text{star} + \text{circle} = 09$$

$$\text{moon} + \text{cross} + \text{moon} + \text{cross} = 24$$

$$\text{star} + \text{cross} + \text{star} + \text{cross} + \text{star} = 25$$

WEEK 20 – SKILL BUILDING

WEEK 20 – PRACTICE WORK

DAY 1 – MONDAY

TIME: _____min _____sec   Accuracy _____/8

1	2	3	4	5	6	7	8
100	390	344	333	120	156	253	153
85	53	95	30	81	53	72	49
274	280	159	297	240	294	289	113
46	75	254	98	54	125	- 511	16
40	29	39	84	70	47	95	92
35	18	20	29	36	64	02	- 423

20:1
© SAI Speed Math Academy, USA

DAY 2 – TUESDAY

TIME: _____min _____sec   Accuracy _____/8

1	2	3	4	5	6	7	8
350	337	285	254	320	247	152	115
27	64	53	62	72	82	94	36
185	145	177	154	173	272	139	166
42	82	210	- 10	12	16	- 82	86
67	75	13	133	15	37	11	13
86	22	86	84	19	96	11	- 303

20:2
© SAI Speed Math Academy, USA

WORD MORPHING

Change the first word into the last word. You can change only one letter each step. You cannot change same letter second time.

FIND _____ _____ _____ BEET

ZERO _____ _____ _____ HAVE

DAY 3 – WEDNESDAY

TIME: _____ min _____ sec   Accuracy _____ /8

1	2	3	4	5	6	7	8	
151	375	325	278	396	104	119	313	
89	68	58	18	85	49	28	20	
288	291	162	277	116	154	160	187	
- 218	11	184	- 470	45	187	54	173	20:3
87	87	63	196	12	60	76	66	
104	58	93	206	67	95	65	46	

DAY 4 – THURSDAY

TIME: _____ min _____ sec   Accuracy _____ /8

1	2	3	4	5	6	7	8	
202	270	178	200	125	302	275	161	
77	43	94	47	11	96	29	28	
278	296	184	288	199	126	199	184	
71	19	100	21	95	36	37	245	20:4
134	44	46	138	69	27	99	65	
14	34	45	92	52	17	84	64	

DAY 5 – FRIDAY

TIME: _____ min _____ sec   Accuracy _____ /8

1	2	3	4	5	6	7	8	
353	388	330	231	276	246	257	398	
48	15	65	68	22	42	11	12	
172	292	228	101	241	163	283	283	
93	71	71	09	85	57	76	58	20:5
142	18	33	93	98	78	45	92	
92	14	39	28	61	77	97	11	

WEEK 20 – MIND MATH PRACTICE WORK

Accuracy _____/16 ☆

DAY 1 – MONDAY

1	2	3	4	5	6	7	8
13	37	59	37	46	91	52	11
94	37	81	92	17	75	29	28
79	84	74	68	59	21	59	91
12	60	13	- 05	55	13	21	76
84	16	- 26	69	55	21	15	39
75	84	60	54	24	65	67	54

20:6

© SAI Speed Math Academy, USA

1	2	3	4	5	6	7	8
22	90	36	32	91	96	306	285
81	20	98	86	23	96	35	47
99	36	51	24	36	97	268	168
43	19	94	74	31	80	40	93
56	- 24	- 10	56	47	72	11	117
95	76	37	81	77	36	- 650	99

20:7

© SAI Speed Math Academy, USA

MIRROR IMAGE

Draw mirror image of the picture on the other side of the line next to it.

Accuracy _____/16 ☆

1	2	3	4	5	6	7	8	
27	75	96	54	65	10	83	88	
88	75	11	99	82	87	35	52	
33	86	46	17	29	32	85	87	
76	57	36	92	80	74	22	94	20:8
44	24	- 47	52	- 14	26	11	82	
26	97	74	41	58	21	65	58	

© SAI Speed Math Academy, USA

1	2	3	4	5	6	7	8	
33	12	49	93	83	71	297	80	
74	29	17	25	31	71	19	49	
45	52	12	83	83	82	100	44	
54	41	33	53	- 55	10	88	79	20:9
23	80	66	- 11	98	57	58	- 121	
75	29	85	39	90	38	19	- 131	

© SAI Speed Math Academy, USA

SEPARATE SHAPES
DRAW 4 STRAIGHT LINES TO SEPARATE ARROWS AND GIVE THEM THEIR OWN SPACE.

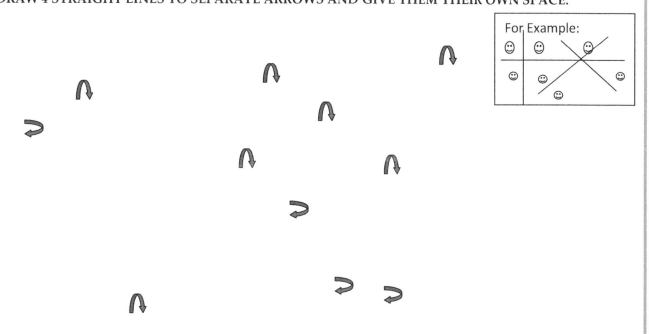

Accuracy _____/16 ☆

1	2	3	4	5	6	7	8
19	43	38	86	29	44	54	66
92	37	13	95	92	89	33	46
63	78	65	74	15	37	69	26
98	13	57	- 44	65	30	53	17
27	48	- 30	98	81	83	99	14
72	83	59	91	- 52	22	71	35

20:10 © SAI Speed Math Academy, USA

1	2	3	4	5	6	7	8
64	32	37	99	58	89	145	237
16	24	81	85	86	94	46	98
90	24	38	46	45	77	253	255
28	94	- 23	12	77	81	25	65
32	- 44	19	33	50	31	145	- 601
13	83	63	53	15	45	84	- 54

20:11 © SAI Speed Math Academy, USA

WORD LIST

List words with five letters or more that **ends** with a 'ick' as in 'slick' and 'ack' as in 'back'. Write a story and try to use at least 5 words from the list in your story.

_____ _____ _____ _____

_____ _____ _____ _____

_____ _____ _____ _____

_____ _____ _____ _____

_____ _____ _____ _____

Accuracy _____/16 ☆

1	2	3	4	5	6	7	8	
76	40	18	85	27	41	27	94	
54	21	57	72	21	90	81	92	
55	83	31	24	39	43	46	25	20:12
62	14	58	- 81	47	89	25	88	
97	21	- 44	73	72	34	60	93	
31	21	67	50	77	56	32	59	

© SAI Speed Math Academy, USA

1	2	3	4	5	6	7	8	
76	13	37	82	77	49	173	48	
83	89	65	38	86	63	182	216	
87	41	82	95	62	26	41	89	20:13
26	89	07	52	- 11	24	61	- 222	
43	- 30	15	80	65	85	- 115	38	
89	26	45	74	22	53	- 142	01	

© SAI Speed Math Academy, USA

MISSING NUMBERS

Fill in the missing numbers

Use numbers 0 to 9 and fill in the empty cells.
Clues:
1. Rows add up to the total on the right.
2. Columns add up to the total at the bottom.
3. Diagonal cells up to the total shown in the top and bottom cells.
4. Numbers can repeat within a row or column.

Left grid:

				23
3	9			23
		7	6	21
	3	4		12
7			1	20
20	17	24	15	9

Right grid:

				13
	5	0		5
2		7		16
	6			18
0		6	0	14
6	22	21	4	11

Accuracy _____/16 ⭐

1	2	3	4	5	6	7	8
69	25	74	49	13	21	72	14
42	33	49	30	48	19	72	55
19	71	27	15	78	53	53	20
96	41	42	- 33	62	- 30	22	61
81	51	26	86	58	23	74	33
83	12	13	55	96	24	97	31

20:14 © SAI Speed Math Academy, USA

1	2	3	4	5	6	7	8
36	28	36	96	17	30	391	128
44	90	20	12	32	65	66	81
54	69	19	88	15	19	110	94
22	69	55	15	48	61	- 464	55
33	10	76	14	14	94	36	55
71	22	63	61	13	46	11	- 411

20:15 © SAI Speed Math Academy, USA

SHAPE PUZZLE

Find out what each shape is worth.

Clue: Study 2nd equation and see how the facts given here can be used to solve other equations.

😊 + 😊 + 😊 + ⭕ = 23

⭕ + ⭕ + ⭕ + ⭕ = 32

⊘ – 😊 + ⭕ = 13

⊘ =___   😊 =___   ⭕ =___

WEEK 20 – DICTATION

DICTATION: Dictation is when teacher or parent calls out a series of numbers and the child listens to the numbers and does the calculation in mind or on the abacus.

DO 6 PROBLEMS A DAY and write answers below.

Students: Try to calculate the dictated problems in mind.

Teachers: Dictate problems from abacus math part of this week's homework.

1	2	3	4	5	6	7	8	9	10

11	12	13	14	15	16	17	18	19	20

21	22	23	24	25	26	27	28	29	30

WORD SEARCH

```
J A S P E T U N I A L I Y E L I L L
T U E N I M S A J R O E L S I R I J
H I B I R O S E S A S T U L I P L A
F L O W E R S L B H R H D A D Z A S
L S I I R R I O Z Y M E K I L I C E
O R C H I D B T M L A D V L N N T N
T U T O O L B U Z I G Z Z O R I L I
T O R F E G A S D L L B G N L A I E
U O F R I C G D D L A E P G K C P R
S A I L A H D Z I Y B K K A S T E R
D B S U C S I B I H D A H M F L O W
```

FLOWERS
DAFFODILS
ROSES
LOTUS
JASMINE
LILLY
TULIP
HIBISCUS
ASTER
BEGONIA
DHALIA
CLOVER
IRIS
LILAC
MAGNOLIA
ORCHID
PETUNIA
SAGE
ZINIA
MYRTLE

EXTRA PRACTICE

1	2	3	4	5	6	7	8	9	10
33	32	50	34	62	54	48	98	44	20
26	74	93	31	20	80	80	78	67	79
52	44	66	89	21	35	37	65	91	38
72	68	85	- 44	28	07	38	57	72	19
12	47	47	68	33	66	84	11	43	- 51
98	34	31	61	- 53	68	14	71	78	09

EP:1 © SAI Speed Math Academy, USA

1	2	3	4	5	6	7	8	9	10
79	41	21	29	45	33	62	55	98	15
27	83	17	30	90	35	20	81	33	26
63	61	40	67	12	85	52	10	55	80
39	49	87	74	- 03	89	29	38	- 21	41
32	73	26	56	66	14	73	60	- 45	29
76	56	48	- 14	57	43	19	25	70	10

EP:2 © SAI Speed Math Academy, USA

1	2	3	4	5	6	7	8	9	10
47	72	88	96	26	91	74	75	90	56
34	77	89	34	47	37	45	13	46	41
45	80	10	67	41	37	72	50	11	40
74	46	59	15	45	- 23	36	20	26	- 02
26	- 53	43	37	39	31	15	32	23	83
34	79	19	57	62	40	98	18	97	31

EP:3 © SAI Speed Math Academy, USA

1	2	3	4	5	6	7	8	9	10	
79	87	14	56	22	26	64	231	354	337	
61	50	29	90	26	62	40	72	78	22	
33	25	85	23	12	94	18	190	280	151	
44	92	46	- 06	98	12	77	80	88	224	EP:4
94	89	- 21	84	89	35	26	77	96	48	
60	50	77	13	34	45	56	32	22	18	

1	2	3	4	5	6	7	8	9	10	
51	39	48	54	64	58	79	324	203	274	
17	53	59	49	75	92	62	23	78	79	
89	32	99	51	78	95	66	148	295	266	
66	10	96	43	59	90	82	34	- 05	235	EP:5
79	52	34	75	20	59	27	132	57	92	
68	54	59	60	16	32	10	41	76	49	

1	2	3	4	5	6	7	8	9	10	
48	94	42	58	23	24	49	266	358	250	
60	16	72	72	32	21	13	65	93	45	
18	66	86	48	41	48	90	299	180	206	
85	73	83	81	- 05	17	36	96	64	187	EP:6
71	68	74	41	36	55	99	112	95	11	
47	74	25	33	20	95	24	19	50	02	

1	2	3	4	5	6	7	8	9	10
43	67	53	14	22	66	12	269	337	321
21	36	46	70	60	11	78	41	93	10
61	82	28	81	29	12	54	233	262	234
20	23	12	08	82	12	49	89	63	208
77	17	20	44	45	89	49	95	49	79
35	57	41	29	15	72	70	19	10	30

EP:7

1	2	3	4	5	6	7	8	9	10
15	69	76	71	19	42	23	359	308	142
54	68	90	65	67	24	62	26	84	64
31	93	35	60	80	14	50	180	145	151
92	58	25	- 92	- 54	37	27	11	59	149
89	10	31	55	47	92	24	33	70	25
87	42	33	45	41	52	67	42	28	50

EP:8

1	2	3	4	5	6	7	8	9	10
18	91	44	96	59	69	49	122	211	294
18	71	53	22	71	23	19	89	80	23
86	81	58	51	37	99	97	185	268	106
33	60	11	74	- 02	22	32	18	78	149
41	27	94	22	88	48	72	187	16	33
69	55	71	37	91	42	51	60	17	98

EP:9

1	2	3	4	5	6	7	8	9	10	
72	35	46	67	42	49	99	358	115	180	
37	21	90	40	74	80	81	88	12	12	
59	17	21	57	47	57	27	228	229	168	
02	35	76	- 40	13	66	08	71	73	29	EP:10
10	77	86	51	49	16	78	184	11	111	
79	59	23	28	27	11	13	34	42	- 200	

1	2	3	4	5	6	7	8	9	10	
97	49	43	52	46	99	34	280	161	338	
16	45	96	97	10	73	79	19	47	13	
29	87	82	81	67	67	76	274	187	208	
80	61	57	19	34	94	- 34	46	14	220	EP:11
83	15	54	52	- 13	24	- 21	58	58	91	
75	45	16	24	56	- 46	16	30	77	49	

1	2	3	4	5	6	7	8	9	10	
43	73	25	47	34	60	83	218	312	241	
69	13	43	46	63	39	73	24	81	32	
20	61	63	72	66	60	36	282	185	197	
97	76	44	94	96	21	69	- 101	- 220	58	EP:12
30	61	- 31	41	62	81	11	75	30	- 111	
95	46	17	76	34	55	45	15	116	87	

END OF LEVEL 2 – TEST

CALCULATE ON ABACUS

AIM FOR ACCURACY

Use Abacus

1	2	3	4	5	6	7	8	9	10	
43	79	11	78	72	87	70	83	32	42	Test:1
41	67	31	11	76	86	73	50	58	19	
40	74	34	32	22	68	16	22	63	42	
69	91	65	63	99	69	41	95	97	38	
13	45	65	87	62	64	84	27	71	81	
50	35	45	58	92	33	96	27	72	59	

1	2	3	4	5	6	7	8	9	10	
12	67	34	48	77	29	45	71	70	41	Test:2
64	53	95	34	11	74	70	23	66	60	
92	42	95	66	17	52	56	44	68	81	
83	68	91	52	36	- 31	37	50	69	91	
13	70	31	98	63	43	69	- 23	- 42	75	
16	97	56	13	28	35	56	87	65	29	

1	2	3	4	5	6	7	8	9	10	
13	61	80	23	67	95	72	81	22	89	Test:3
51	81	87	64	13	22	81	69	68	11	
94	72	74	43	57	24	33	92	20	64	
- 46	72	63	55	- 22	21	45	95	39	46	
55	99	51	19	94	25	22	17	11	39	
85	- 75	- 24	44	42	- 46	52	21	58	55	

Test:4

1	2	3	4	5	6	7	8	9	10
56	49	21	83	11	37	37	38	46	34
51	47	66	62	88	67	91	52	93	59
90	25	98	37	81	45	51	67	52	86
13	92	68	28	14	19	61	83	71	75
13	58	35	88	57	36	57	49	14	12
82	51	15	54	31	47	22	11	- 72	- 24

Test:5

1	2	3	4	5	6	7	8	9	10
55	70	98	41	77	32	54	44	69	85
79	49	78	31	45	93	27	86	17	45
46	44	36	18	43	42	68	35	43	82
86	86	76	55	63	58	88	93	11	56
48	12	13	31	14	29	64	42	56	17
- 12	- 41	16	25	13	88	99	54	- 94	19

Test:6

1	2	3	4	5	6	7	8	9	10
215	277	816	191	105	687	264	373	196	327
81	681	- 414	65	51	- 243	54	97	65	- 104
115	- 542	49	62	56	55	188	180	- 120	131
36	86	16	22	72	05	45	- 510	14	- 120
55	65	13	56	54	- 400	158	155	- 22	31
18	58	42	107	163	296	- 305	105	67	- 264

MIND MATH

1	2	3	4	5	6	7	8	9	10	
78	81	57	97	14	92	99	29	76	26	
19	13	37	29	97	90	14	27	56	70	
15	17	17	98	59	97	21	- 15	95	32	
32	50	25	26	- 30	- 09	55	22	31	12	Test:7
11	- 30	15	06	15	67	61	87	28	35	
95	59	- 21	- 14	- 44	- 33	- 40	48	30	- 42	
										© SAI Speed Math Academy, USA

1	2	3	4	5	6	7	8	9	10	
71	17	60	13	59	45	52	178	392	140	
99	45	92	23	80	69	83	70	- 162	39	
08	85	23	80	45	61	15	09	28	21	
- 63	- 44	- 31	79	- 22	65	85	- 245	- 37	58	Test:8
85	70	16	08	15	55	60	35	135	- 213	
02	85	94	23	25	- 81	07	155	25	17	
										© SAI Speed Math Academy, USA

DICTATION

Calculate dictation problems on abacus.

1	2	3	4	5	6	7	8	9	10

Calculate dictation problems in mind.

1	2	3	4	5	6	7	8	9	10

ANSWER KEY

WEEK 11 – LESSON 10

1	2	3	4	5	6	7	8	
62	84	31	96	105	130	55	58	11:1

1	2	3	4	5	6	7	8	
148	132	174	147	60	52	122	209	11:2

1	2	3	4	5	6	7	8	
21	113	206	68	115	00	145	123	11:3

1	2	3	4	5	6	7	8	
52	127	130	150	114	153	590	210	11:4

1	2	3	4	5	6	7	8	
34	80	152	62	10	85	41	77	11:5

1	2	3	4	5	6	7	8	
151	00	23	195	126	64	653	132	11:6

1	2	3	4	5	6	7	8	
103	00	56	30	121	138	152	205	11:7

1	2	3	4	5	6	7	8	
250	61	112	124	260	353	209	200	11:8

1	2	3	4	5	6	7	8	
150	68	119	51	141	66	55	150	11:9

1	2	3	4	5	7	6	8	
79	12	64	200	102	333	105	350	11:10

1	2	3	4	5	6	7	8	
100	40	71	201	228	215	140	254	11:11

1	2	3	4	5	6	7	8	
100	41	150	444	320	353	000	225	11:12

LESSON 10 – MIND MATH PRACTICE WORK

1	2	3	4	5	6	7	8	9	10	
09	24	65	92	71	107	110	100	99	109	11:13

1	2	3	4	5	6	7	8	9	10	
112	82	109	154	146	51	19	120	103	135	11:14

1	2	3	4	5	6	7	8	9	10	
74	131	102	151	150	111	13	70	134	20	11:15

1	2	3	4	5	6	7	8	9	10	
144	101	170	120	31	170	141	03	110	11	11:16

1	2	3	4	5	6	7	8	9	10	
42	111	163	100	151	151	30	150	63	151	11:17

1	2	3	4	5	6	7	8	9	10	
74	121	131	120	110	155	140	220	141	103	11:18

WORD SEARCH

R	E	P	A	**P**	E	T	I	R	**W**
P			S	K	O	O	**B**		**P**
A	**G**	R							E
D	A	E	**F**	R	I	E	N	D	N
	R	H							C
D	C	**E**	R	A	S	E	R	I	I
E	A	**S**	P	O	R	T	S	L	L
N	E								B
		T	**D**	A	N	C	E	R	A
S	T	O	R	Y	R	E	E	**P**	**L**

SUDOKU

3	5	6	4	1	2
1	4	2	6	5	3
5	1	4	2	3	6
6	2	3	5	4	1
2	3	5	1	6	4
4	6	1	3	2	5

www.abacus-math.com

WEEK 12 – LESSON 11

1	2	3	4	5	6	7	8	
42	161	112	72	110	157	163	115	12:1

1	2	3	4	5	6	7	8	
150	111	155	150	105	154	143	21	12:2

1	2	3	4	5	6	7	8	
52	63	130	133	115	83	235	141	12:3

1	2	3	4	5	6	7	8	
133	53	133	231	140	153	272	325	12:4

1	2	3	4	5	6	7	8	
183	49	48	103	138	142	140	134	12:5

1	2	3	4	5	6	7	8	
125	151	154	00	200	100	552	20	12:6

1	2	3	4	5	6	7	8	
50	107	104	120	102	100	140	101	12:7

1	2	3	4	5	6	7	8	
141	151	104	113	110	440	434	34	12:8

1	2	3	4	5	6	7	8	
124	63	112	140	75	118	103	50	12:9

1	2	3	4	5	7	6	8	
151	96	142	140	225	350	240	410	12:10

1	2	3	4	5	6	7	8	
100	99	30	153	250	62	00	356	12:11

1	2	3	4	5	6	7	8	
132	152	20	102	95	250	250	121	12:12

LESSON 11 – MIND MATH PRACTICE WORK

1	2	3	4	5	6	7	8	9	10	
62	72	92	83	59	115	55	101	115	101	12:13

1	2	3	4	5	6	7	8	9	10	
111	96	163	115	30	13	82	125	131	152	12:14

1	2	3	4	5	6	7	8	9	10	
132	126	150	140	144	141	133	104	175	166	12:15

1	2	3	4	5	6	7	8	9	10	
100	120	112	142	40	123	113	63	112	140	12:16

1	2	3	4	5	6	7	8	9	10	
30	42	135	150	140	141	00	155	103	138	12:17

1	2	3	4	5	6	7	8	9	10	
100	81	101	140	245	51	50	154	11	151	12:18

SUDOKU

5	2	3	1	6	4
4	6	1	5	3	2
1	4	5	3	2	6
6	3	2	4	1	5
3	5	6	2	4	1
2	1	4	6	5	3

MIRROR IMAGE

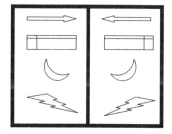

WEEK 13 – LESSON 12

1	2	3	4	5	6	7	8	
27	72	81	56	21	150	51	150	13:1

1	2	3	4	5	6	7	8	
120	132	112	105	144	100	55	154	13:2

1	2	3	4	5	6	7	8	
118	145	112	114	119	129	113	30	13:3

1	2	3	4	5	6	7	8	
205	132	110	151	162	110	228	44	13:4

1	2	3	4	5	6	7	8	
13	155	151	76	50	100	40	252	13:5

1	2	3	4	5	6	7	8	
150	207	215	152	140	111	552	270	13:6

1	2	3	4	5	6	7	8	
90	46	109	214	240	152	52	144	13:7

1	2	3	4	5	6	7	8	
109	150	24	165	201	255	610	743	13:8

1	2	3	4	5	6	7	8	
162	305	140	253	211	254	212	650	13:9

1	2	3	4	5	7	6	8	
163	40	50	250	120	124	533	541	13:10

1	2	3	4	5	6	7	8	
234	264	287	160	206	160	134	534	13:11

1	2	3	4	5	6	7	8	
101	172	34	150	102	121	326	467	13:12

LESSON 12 – MIND MATH PRACTICE WORK

1	2	3	4	5	6	7	8	9	10	
49	59	71	70	115	91	100	73	114	130	13:13

1	2	3	4	5	6	7	8	9	10	
130	94	137	25	44	14	123	150	153	250	13:14

1	2	3	4	5	6	7	8	9	10	
111	151	120	138	171	173	150	63	152	150	13:15

1	2	3	4	5	6	7	8	9	10	
58	11	133	200	198	111	92	130	113	150	13:16

1	2	3	4	5	6	7	8	9	10	
152	155	100	162	211	116	40	150	160	30	13:17

1	2	3	4	5	6	7	8	9	10	
151	154	124	130	161	153	215	130	151	102	13:18

SUDOKU

1	5	6	4	2	3
3	2	4	6	5	1
4	1	3	2	6	5
5	6	2	3	1	4
6	4	1	5	3	2
2	3	5	1	4	6

MIRROR IMAGE

1	2	3	4	5	6	7	8	
50	41	101	81	111	151	111	102	14:1

1	2	3	4	5	6	7	8	
119	110	20	110	105	30	151	151	14:2

1	2	3	4	5	6	7	8	
116	154	100	180	146	151	130	261	14:3

1	2	3	4	5	6	7	8	
176	251	204	155	252	515	450	610	14:4

1	2	3	4	5	6	7	8	
130	165	187	140	141	114	161	240	14:5

1	2	3	4	5	6	7	8	
155	185	240	113	123	251	41	660	14:6

1	2	3	4	5	6	7	8	
120	195	66	203	131	143	155	60	14:7

1	2	3	4	5	6	7	8	
131	349	134	173	180	105	67	510	14:8

1	2	3	4	5	6	7	8	
175	122	132	110	110	245	246	154	14:9

1	2	3	4	5	7	6	8	
132	114	333	190	100	287	312	253	14:10

1	2	3	4	5	6	7	8	
246	254	154	210	101	192	135	281	14:11

1	2	3	4	5	6	7	8	
110	291	122	100	154	576	561	145	14:12

LESSON 13 – MIND MATH PRACTICE WORK

1	2	3	4	5	6	7	8	9	10	
43	60	126	20	123	101	118	121	175	161	14:13

1	2	3	4	5	6	7	8	9	10	
23	62	61	50	110	129	111	105	251	251	14:14

1	2	3	4	5	6	7	8	9	10	
120	37	140	120	122	61	116	141	310	41	14:15

1	2	3	4	5	6	7	8	9	10	
102	141	110	134	151	33	131	102	120	161	14:16

1	2	3	4	5	6	7	8	9	10	
112	86	143	214	108	12	108	112	122	153	14:17

1	2	3	4	5	6	7	8	9	10	
131	161	90	23	253	103	30	306	274	21	14:18

NUMBER BLOCK

09

1	4	3	6	14
2	8	0	5	15
7	0	5	4	16
3	0	9	1	13

13	12	17	16	15

NUMBER BLOCK

15

0	1	5	9	15
5	7	4	8	24
6	2	4	0	12
0	1	3	1	05

11	11	16	18	12

WEEK 15 – LESSON 14

1	2	3	4	5	6	7	8	
90	00	140	140	120	111	120	100	15:1

1	2	3	4	5	6	7	8	
100	150	150	110	154	105	150	114	15:2

1	2	3	4	5	6	7	8	
62	110	112	50	101	139	250	150	15:3

1	2	3	4	5	6	7	8	
60	33	112	109	350	520	260	270	15:4

1	2	3	4	5	6	7	8	
50	114	235	210	150	110	20	114	15:5

1	2	3	4	5	6	7	8	
210	209	261	204	240	140	610	840	15:6

1	2	3	4	5	6	7	8	
132	116	238	164	80	80	110	40	15:7

1	2	3	4	5	6	7	8	
70	148	200	220	506	230	22	514	15:8

1	2	3	4	5	6	7	8	
345	254	143	160	100	150	00	111	15:9

1	2	3	4	5	6	7	8	
100	173	220	250	50	585	353	00	15:10

1	2	3	4	5	6	7	8	
171	111	110	114	146	60	214	150	15:11

1	2	3	4	5	6	7	8	
77	150	102	105	01	650	505	501	15:12

LESSON 14 – MIND MATH PRACTICE WORK

1	2	3	4	5	6	7	8	9	10	
66	30	60	105	150	105	00	114	155	161	15:13

1	2	3	4	5	6	7	8	9	10	
110	20	110	130	60	111	167	140	100	122	15:14

1	2	3	4	5	6	7	8	9	10	
112	101	110	26	127	106	93	50	130	157	15:15

1	2	3	4	5	6	7	8	9	10	
110	150	123	54	120	00	250	209	44	220	15:16

1	2	3	4	5	6	7	8	9	10	
80	126	250	100	155	140	200	100	111	110	15:17

1	2	3	4	5	6	7	8	9	10	
100	110	122	104	100	150	120	112	00	10	15:18

WEEK 16 – LESSON 15

1	2	3	4	5	6	7	8	9	10	
100	110	90	100	101	111	101	91	102	112	16:S:5

1	2	3	4	5	6	7	8	9	10	
92	102	103	113	93	103	104	114	104	94	16:S:6

1	2	3	4	5	6	7	8	9	10	
105	115	95	105	106	116	106	96	107	117	16:S:7

1	2	3	4	5	6	7	8	9	10	
97	107	108	118	108	98	104	114	94	104	16:S:8

1	2	3	4	5	6	7	8	9	10	
104	113	104	93	102	113	94	102	102	104	16:S:9

1	2	3	4	5	6	7	8	9	10	
504	503	504	603	602	413	503	602	502	604	16:S:10

1	2	3	4	5	6	7	8	
100	110	90	100	101	111	101	91	16:1

1	2	3	4	5	6	7	8	
101	110	91	100	201	121	100	111	16:2

1	2	3	4	5	6	7	8	
188	235	201	214	161	155	30	126	16:3

1	2	3	4	5	6	7	8	
201	100	114	31	400	402	600	304	16:4

1	2	3	4	5	6	7	8	
103	112	93	191	201	111	92	104	16:5

1	2	3	4	5	6	7	8	
163	165	204	00	200	502	100	100	16:6

1	2	3	4	5	6	7	8	
101	113	93	103	102	116	103	94	16:7

1	2	3	4	5	6	7	8	
150	200	300	109	102	104	502	232	16:8

1	2	3	4	5	6	7	8	
100	104	105	51	144	105	171	01	16:9

1	2	3	4	5	6	7	8	
239	67	54	102	121	501	331	303	16:10

1	2	3	4	5	6	7	8	
127	163	31	153	116	100	100	210	16:11

1	2	3	4	5	6	7	8	
231	244	142	11	181	300	811	130	16:12

UNSCRAMBLE

Basketball
Soccer
Baseball
Swimming
Fencing
Skipping
Polo
Figure Skating
Gymnastics

LESSON 15 – MIND MATH PRACTICE WORK

1	2	3	4	5	6	7	8	9	10	
105	146	127	108	109	110	111	112	137	150	16:13

1	2	3	4	5	6	7	8	9	10	
143	172	138	128	122	116	114	148	144	100	16:14

1	2	3	4	5	6	7	8	9	10	
100	138	154	157	168	210	130	102	64	154	16:15

1	2	3	4	5	6	7	8	9	10	
76	113	104	112	100	148	128	105	254	552	16:16

1	2	3	4	5	6	7	8	9	10	
12	208	111	215	148	102	101	100	250	101	16:17

1	2	3	4	5	6	7	8	9	10	
156	102	65	105	127	141	601	504	300	401	16:18

WORD MORPHING

fig – big – beg – bee
saw – paw – pad – pod
cry – fry – fly – flu
cot – pot – pat – pan

WEEK 17 – SKILL BUILDING

1	2	3	4	5	6	7	8	
94	136	104	154	210	223	205	31	17:1

1	2	3	4	5	6	7	8	
256	203	141	400	403	204	241	500	17:2

1	2	3	4	5	6	7	8	
150	120	181	258	215	141	124	202	17:3

1	2	3	4	5	6	7	8	
175	00	180	346	131	450	100	302	17:4

1	2	3	4	5	6	7	8	
202	225	226	179	115	100	123	204	17:5

1	2	3	4	5	6	7	8	
139	168	163	526	100	506	310	236	17:6

1	2	3	4	5	6	7	8	
175	140	164	185	219	130	85	120	17:7

1	2	3	4	5	6	7	8	
200	32	351	502	250	202	490	505	17:8

1	2	3	4	5	6	7	8	
356	162	113	231	165	134	00	164	17:9

1	2	3	4	5	6	7	8	
201	200	130	206	280	509	500	650	17:10

WEEK 17 – MIND MATH PRACTICE WORK

1	2	3	4	5	6	7	8	9	10	
123	98	150	200	152	100	115	43	211	200	17:11

1	2	3	4	5	6	7	8	9	10	
39	42	133	150	50	140	51	133	150	500	17:12

1	2	3	4	5	6	7	8	9	10	
110	130	145	210	234	109	21	60	241	351	17:13

1	2	3	4	5	6	7	8	9	10	
132	116	238	164	210	209	205	234	200	426	17:14

1	2	3	4	5	6	7	8	9	10	
127	186	100	206	100	101	104	252	302	201	17:15

1	2	3	4	5	6	7	8	9	10	
110	200	104	40	111	146	161	102	506	378	17:16

WORD MORPHING
zoro – zero – hero – herd – heed
make – mike – mine – pine – pint

WEEK 18 – SKILL BUILDING

1	2	3	4	5	6	7	8	
114	102	256	345	303	303	445	320	18:1

1	2	3	4	5	6	7	8	
277	364	320	819	554	701	503	461	18:2

1	2	3	4	5	6	7	8	
232	231	402	112	397	248	300	160	18:3

1	2	3	4	5	6	7	8	
303	318	265	463	500	500	00	22	18:4

1	2	3	4	5	6	7	8	
349	314	183	221	201	200	353	222	18:5

1	2	3	4	5	6	7	8	
252	154	231	900	806	153	314	00	18:6

1	2	3	4	5	6	7	8	
343	256	320	252	161	264	409	262	18:7

1	2	3	4	5	6	7	8	
309	330	130	550	100	250	509	504	18:8

1	2	3	4	5	6	7	8	
411	337	352	198	260	156	320	289	18:9

1	2	3	4	5	6	7	8	
231	205	150	10	300	20	551	549	18:10

WEEK 18 – MIND MATH PRACTICE WORK

1	2	3	4	5	6	7	8	9	10	
288	113	218	143	244	91	74	160	63	300	18:11

1	2	3	4	5	6	7	8	9	10	
311	212	195	99	110	204	71	00	450	00	18:12

1	2	3	4	5	6	7	8	9	10	
226	246	200	230	319	304	250	202	264	362	18:13

1	2	3	4	5	6	7	8	9	10	
120	155	145	210	246	212	140	60	01	500	18:14

1	2	3	4	5	6	7	8	9	10	
139	168	163	244	142	200	32	101	470	373	18:15

1	2	3	4	5	6	7	8	9	10	
244	140	164	185	330	209	125	240	123	518	18:16

RIDDLE
4. Your name
5. Wet
6. Coin

WORD MORPHING
fan – ban – bin – bit
see – bee – bet – bat
big – bag – bat – sat
bud – bad – bat – say

MIRROR IMAGE

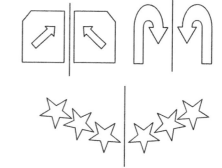

SEPARATE SHAPES

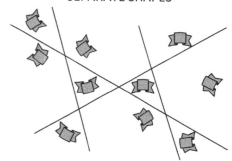

WEEK 19 – SKILL BUILDING

1	2	3	4	5	6	7	8	
345	138	252	288	228	405	234	322	19:1

1	2	3	4	5	6	7	8	
200	502	01	389	392	500	00	554	19:2

1	2	3	4	5	6	7	8	
348	487	337	299	294	303	302	223	19:3

1	2	3	4	5	6	7	8	
400	357	303	551	00	405	110	900	19:4

1	2	3	4	5	6	7	8	
340	292	320	210	245	300	283	307	19:5

1	2	3	4	5	6	7	8	
451	277	698	600	00	174	202	174	19:6

1	2	3	4	5	6	7	8	
303	305	449	204	234	170	143	323	19:7

1	2	3	4	5	6	7	8	
00	402	371	00	351	612	369	100	19:8

1	2	3	4	5	6	7	8	
323	269	244	352	351	230	387	305	19:9

1	2	3	4	5	6	7	8	
505	202	41	554	00	750	365	00	19:10

WEEK 19 – MIND MATH PRACTICE WORK

1	2	3	4	5	6	7	8	9	10	
142	120	121	124	115	100	144	113	544	326	19:11

1	2	3	4	5	6	7	8	9	10	
149	225	235	203	153	112	113	144	231	410	19:12

1	2	3	4	5	6	7	8	9	10	
162	113	231	165	134	00	164	144	00	701	19:13

1	2	3	4	5	6	7	8	9	10	
130	84	100	94	136	104	104	402	503	200	19:14

1	2	3	4	5	6	7	8	9	10	
144	280	287	254	184	268	225	371	502	220	19:15

1	2	3	4	5	6	7	8	9	10	
346	100	289	120	122	176	301	512	11	427	19:16

RIDDLE

1. Fire
2. Bo(w) tie
3. Sawdust

WORD MORPHING

pike – pile – mile – male – mall
kids – kiss – miss – mist – must

SHAPES PUZZLE

 = 03   ◎ = 06

 = 04   ✚ = 08

MIRROR IMAGE

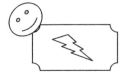 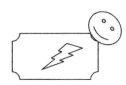

NUMBER BLOCK

				13
4	5	5	0	14
4	5	1	9	19
1	7	1	7	16
5	4	3	5	17
14	21	10	21	15

NUMBER BLOCK

				15
5	2	4	0	11
8	6	5	6	25
5	8	7	4	24
2	3	9	5	19
20	19	25	15	23

www.abacus-math.com

WEEK 20 – SKILL BUILDING

1	2	3	4	5	6	7	8	
580	845	911	871	601	739	200	00	20:1

1	2	3	4	5	6	7	8	
757	725	824	677	611	750	325	113	20:2

1	2	3	4	5	6	7	8	
501	890	885	505	721	649	502	805	20:3

1	2	3	4	5	6	7	8	
776	706	647	786	551	604	723	747	20:4

1	2	3	4	5	6	7	8	
900	798	766	530	783	663	769	854	20:5

WORD MORPHING

find – bind – bend – bent – beet
zero – hero – here – hare – have

MIRROR IMAGE

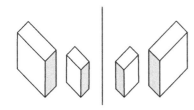

SEPARATE SHAPES

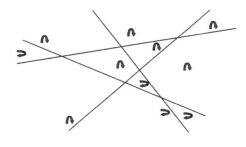

SHAPES PUZZLE

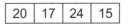 = 05   ◎ = 08

⊘ = 10

WEEK 20 – MIND MATH PRACTICE WORK

1	2	3	4	5	6	7	8	
357	318	261	315	256	286	243	299	20:6

1	2	3	4	5	6	7	8	
396	217	306	353	305	477	10	809	20:7

1	2	3	4	5	6	7	8	
294	414	216	355	300	250	301	461	20:8

1	2	3	4	5	6	7	8	
304	243	262	282	330	329	581	00	20:9

1	2	3	4	5	6	7	8	
371	302	202	400	230	305	379	204	20:10

1	2	3	4	5	6	7	8	
243	213	215	328	331	417	698	00	20:11

1	2	3	4	5	6	7	8	
375	200	187	223	283	353	271	45 1	20:12

1	2	3	4	5	6	7	8	
404	228	251	421	301	300	200	170	20:13

1	2	3	4	5	6	7	8	
390	233	231	202	355	110	390	214	20:14

1	2	3	4	5	6	7	8	
260	288	269	286	139	315	150	02	20:15

NUMBER BLOCK

23

3	9	5	6	23
7	1	7	6	21
3	3	4	2	12
7	4	8	1	20

20	17	24	15	9

NUMBER BLOCK

13

0	5	0	0	5
2	3	7	4	16
4	6	8	0	18
0	8	6	0	14

6	22	21	4	11

WEEK 20

WORD SEARCH

		P	E	T	U	N	I	A			E			L
	E	N	I	M	S	A	J				L	S	I	R	I
		R	O	S	E	S			T	U	L	I	P	L
F	L	O	W	E	R	S	L		R		A		Z	A
			I	O		Y		E		I		I	C
O	R	C	H	I	D		T	M	L		V	L	N	N
		O		U		L			O		I
	F	E	G	A	S		L		G	N	L	A
	F				L	E		G		C
A	I	L	A	H	D		Y	B		A	S	T	E	R
D	S	U	C	S	I	B	I	H		M

EXTRA PRACTICE

1	2	3	4	5	6	7	8	9	10	
293	299	372	239	111	310	301	380	395	114	EP:1

1	2	3	4	5	6	7	8	9	10	
316	363	239	242	267	299	255	269	190	201	EP:2

1	2	3	4	5	6	7	8	9	10	
260	301	308	306	260	213	340	208	293	249	EP:3

1	2	3	4	5	6	7	8	9	10	
371	393	230	260	281	274	281	682	918	800	EP:4

1	2	3	4	5	6	7	8	9	10	
370	240	395	332	312	426	326	702	704	995	EP:5

1	2	3	4	5	6	7	8	9	10	
329	391	382	333	147	260	311	857	840	701	EP:6

EXTRA PRACTICE

1	2	3	4	5	6	7	8	9	10	
257	282	200	246	253	262	312	746	814	882	EP:7

1	2	3	4	5	6	7	8	9	10	
368	340	290	204	200	261	253	651	694	581	EP:8

1	2	3	4	5	6	7	8	9	10	
265	385	331	302	344	303	320	661	670	703	EP:9

1	2	3	4	5	6	7	8	9	10	
259	244	342	203	252	279	306	963	482	300	EP:10

1	2	3	4	5	6	7	8	9	10	
380	302	348	325	200	311	150	707	544	919	EP:11

1	2	3	4	5	6	7	8	9	10	
354	330	161	376	355	316	317	513	504	504	EP:12

www.abacus-math.com

END OF LEVEL 2 – TEST

1	2	3	4	5	6	7	8	9	10	
256	391	251	329	423	407	380	304	393	281	Test:1

1	2	3	4	5	6	7	8	9	10	
280	397	402	311	232	202	333	252	296	377	Test:2

1	2	3	4	5	6	7	8	9	10	
252	310	331	248	251	141	305	375	218	304	Test:3

1	2	3	4	5	6	7	8	9	10	
305	322	303	352	282	251	319	300	204	242	Test:4

1	2	3	4	5	6	7	8	9	10	
302	220	317	201	255	342	400	354	102	304	Test:5

1	2	3	4	5	6	7	8	9	10	
520	625	522	503	501	400	404	400	200	01	Test:6

MIND MATH

1	2	3	4	5	6	7	8	9	10	
250	190	130	242	111	304	210	198	316	133	Test:7

1	2	3	4	5	6	7	8	9	10	
202	258	254	226	202	214	302	202	381	62	Test:8

ABOUT SAI SPEED MATH ACADEMY

One subject that is very important for success in this world, along with being able to read and write, is the knowledge of numbers. Math is one subject which requires proficiency from anyone who wants to achieve something in life. A strong foundation and a basic understanding of math is a must to mastering higher levels of math.

We, the family, best friends, and parents of children in elementary school, early on discovered that what our children were learning at school was not enough for them to master the basics of math. Teachers at school, with the resources they had, did the best they could. But, as parents, we had to do more to help them understand the relationship between numbers and basic functions of adding, subtracting, multiplying and dividing. Also, what made us cringe is the fact that our children's attitude towards more complex math was to say, "Oh, we are allowed to use a calculator in class". This did not sit well with us. Even though we did not have a specific system that we followed, each of us could do basic calculations in our minds without looking for a calculator. So, this made us want to do more for our children.

We started to look into the various methods that were available in the marketplace to help our children understand basic math and reduce their dependency on calculators. We came across soroban, a wonderful calculating tool from Japan. Soroban perfectly fits with the base-10 number system used at present and provides a systematic method to follow while calculating in one's mind.

This convinced us and within a short time we were able to work with fluency on the tool. The next step was to introduce it to our children, which we thought was going to be an easy task. It, however, was not. It was next to impossible to find the resources or the curriculum to help us introduce the tool in the correct order. Teaching all the concepts in one sitting and expecting children to apply them to the set of problems we gave them only made them push away the tool in frustration.

However, help comes to those who ask, and to those who are willing to work to achieve their goals. We came across a soroban teacher who helped us by giving us ideas and an outline of how soroban should be introduced. But, we still needed an actual worksheet to give our children to practice on. That is when we decided to come up with practice worksheets of our own design for our kids.

  www.abacus-math.com

Slowly and steadily, practicing with the worksheets that we developed, our children started to get the idea and loved what they could do with a soroban. Soon we realized that they were better with mind math than we were.

Today, 6 years later, all our kids have completed their soroban training and are reaping the benefits of the hard work that they did over the years.

Now, although very happy, we were humbled at the number of requests we got from parents who wanted to know more about our curriculum. We had no way to share our new knowledge with them.

Now, through the introduction of our instruction book and workbooks, that has changed. We want to share everything we know with all the dedicated parents who are interested in teaching soroban to their children. This is our humble attempt to bring a systematic instruction manual and corresponding workbook to help introduce your children to soroban.

What started as a project to help our kids has grown over the years and we are fortunate to say that a number of children have benefitted learning with the same curriculum that we developed for our children.

Thank you for choosing our system to enhance your children's mathematical skills.

We love working on soroban and hope you do too!

List of SAI Speed Math Academy Publications

LEVEL – 1

 Abacus Mind Math Instruction Book Level – 1: Step by Step Guide to Excel at Mind Math with Soroban, a Japanese Abacus
ISBN-13: 978-1941589007

 Abacus Mind Math Level – 1 Workbook 1 of 2: Excel at Mind Math with Soroban, a Japanese Abacus

ISBN-13: 978-1941589014

 Abacus Mind Math Level – 1 Workbook 2 of 2: Excel at Mind Math with Soroban, a Japanese Abacus

ISBN-13: 978-1941589021

LEVEL – 2

 Abacus Mind Math Instruction Book Level – 2: Step by Step Guide to Excel at Mind Math with Soroban, a Japanese Abacus
ISBN-13: 978-1941589038

 Abacus Mind Math Level – 2 Workbook 1 of 2: Excel at Mind Math with Soroban, a Japanese Abacus

ISBN-13: 978-1941589045

 Abacus Mind Math Level – 2 Workbook 2 of 2: Excel at Mind Math with Soroban, a Japanese Abacus

ISBN-13: 978-1941589052

LEVEL – 3

 Abacus Mind Math Instruction Book Level – 3: Step by Step Guide to Excel at Mind Math with Soroban, a Japanese Abacus
ISBN-13: 9781941589069

 Abacus Mind Math Level – 3 Workbook 1 of 2: Excel at Mind Math with Soroban, a Japanese Abacus

ISBN-13: 9781941589076

 Abacus Mind Math Level – 3 Workbook 2 of 2: Excel at Mind Math with Soroban, a Japanese Abacus

ISBN-13: 9781941589083

Continued.....